PENGUIN CANADA

DAILY PLANET

JAY INGRAM has been the host of Discovery Channel Canada's *Daily Planet* since it began in 1995. At the time, it was the only hour-long, prime-time daily science show in the world. Prior to joining Discovery, Jay hosted CBC Radio's national science show, *Quirks and Quarks,* from 1979 to 1992. During that time he won two ACTRA awards, one for best host, and several Canadian Science Writers' awards. He wrote and hosted two CBC Radio documentary series and short radio and television science stories for a variety of programs. He was a contributing editor to *Owl* magazine for ten years and wrote a weekly science column in the *Toronto Star* for twelve. Jay has also written eleven best-selling books, including *The Daily Planet Book of Cool Ideas.*

In 2009 Jay was made a member of the Order of Canada for his contributions toward making complex science accessible to the public—and for his leadership of future generations of science journalists. He has received the Sandford Fleming Medal from the Royal Canadian Institute for his efforts to popularize science, the Royal Society's McNeil Medal for the Public Awareness of Science, and the Michael Smith award from the Natural Sciences and Engineering Research Council. He is a Distinguished Alumnus of the University of Alberta and has received five honorary doctorates.

DAILY PLANET

THE ULTIMATE BOOK OF EVERYDAY SCIENCE

JAY INGRAM

PENGUIN
CANADA

PENGUIN CANADA

Published by the Penguin Group

Penguin Group (Canada), 90 Eglinton Avenue East, Suite 700, Toronto, Ontario, Canada
M4P 2Y3 (a division of Pearson Canada Inc.)

Penguin Group (USA) Inc., 375 Hudson Street, New York, New York 10014, U.S.A.
Penguin Books Ltd, 80 Strand, London WC2R 0RL, England
Penguin Ireland, 25 St Stephen's Green, Dublin 2, Ireland (a division of Penguin Books Ltd)
Penguin Group (Australia), 250 Camberwell Road, Camberwell, Victoria 3124, Australia
(a division of Pearson Australia Group Pty Ltd)
Penguin Books India Pvt Ltd, 11 Community Centre, Panchsheel Park, New Delhi – 110 017, India
Penguin Group (NZ), 67 Apollo Drive, Rosedale, North Shore 0745, Auckland, New Zealand
(a division of Pearson New Zealand Ltd)
Penguin Books (South Africa) (Pty) Ltd, 24 Sturdee Avenue, Rosebank, Johannesburg 2196, South Africa

Penguin Books Ltd, Registered Offices: 80 Strand, London WC2R 0RL, England

First published 2010

2 3 4 5 6 7 8 9 10 (CR)

LIBRARY AND ARCHIVES CANADA CATALOGUING IN PUBLICATION

Ingram, Jay
Daily planet : the ultimate book of everyday science / Jay Ingram.

Includes index.
ISBN 978-0-14-317786-9

1. Science—Miscellanea. I. Title.

Q173.I526 2010   500   C2010-904681-1

Visit the Penguin Group (Canada) website at **www.penguin.ca**

Special and corporate bulk purchase rates available; please see **www.penguin.ca/corporatesales**
or call 1-800-810-3104, ext. 2477 or 2474

This book has been printed on
100-pound Opus Dull paper,
FSC-certified, 30% post-consumer waste,
from the Strategic Paper Group.

To MA

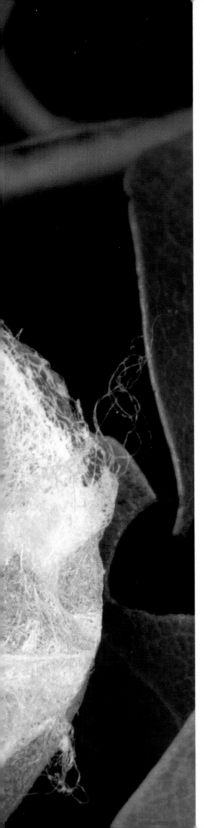

CONTENTS

FOREWORD

THE CHINESE SAYING "A JOURNEY OF A THOUSAND MILES BEGINS WITH A single step" couldn't have been more true when we began production on the world's first daily science show, broadcast on Discovery Channel in Canada on January 1, 1995.

In that moment, all we could think about was producing episode one. We faced the usual technical and production crises that are a reality of daily television: guests who don't show up, stories that collapse because of a lack of visuals, a studio set still under construction.

But the biggest challenge we faced was in our own minds: the knowledge that no one had attempted this before. We were the broadcast pioneers, and there were no experts we could turn to or other television shows we could watch to figure out how it should be done. So we made it up as we went along.

The opinion of my colleagues around the world wasn't encouraging. The head of science at the granddaddy of all English-language public broadcasting, the BBC, wished us a rather bemused and somewhat patronizing "good luck." Others were more direct: "You'll run out of stories." "No one will watch." "The team will run out of energy."

On that first day, however, none of us were really focused on running a television marathon. We weren't even thinking about the next day's episode or getting to the end of the season. All we really hoped was that we'd get a one-hour show on the air seamlessly, without any glitches, and without the network fading to black. In television parlance, we just wanted a clean show.

Well, that's exactly what we delivered. And continued to deliver night after night, year after year. We never ran out of stories or viewers or energy.

Since that day the show has evolved and grown tremendously, thanks to an incredibly devoted and talented editorial and production team; the insatiable curiosity of our audience; and the hundreds of scientists, researchers, and adventurers who appear on the program every year, sharing their passion, their work, and their expertise.

Even the show's title has changed since the first episode. The original title, *@discovery.ca*, was cool and innovative when we launched fifteen years ago. But with the rapid surge in the popularity of the Internet the name soon lost its originality. It was time for a new one. And so, with a more contemporary format that allowed the program to be sold internationally, *Daily Planet* was born.

Despite all the changes, the show's mandate has remained largely the same: to scour the universe each and every day to find the most intriguing, surprising, and exciting discoveries and to share those stories with a loyal audience craving to learn, understand, and be entertained.

Throughout its journey, the program has been blessed with the unwavering support of influential network executives. The show's inspiration came from Trina McQueen, Discovery Channel's first president and general manager in Canada. Susanne Boyce developed the program as a network consultant and then became an important champion in her role as president of Creative, Content and Channels for CTV. Both have encouraged innovation and risk taking, supporting the *Daily Planet* team's efforts to go where no broadcaster has gone before.

On that first day it seemed to all of us that we faced one of the most challenging and scariest mandates ever. But we quickly learned that producing the show could also be a hell of a lot of fun and one of the most rewarding jobs in television.

I hope you'll share in that sense of fun and adventure as you celebrate *Daily Planet*'s fifteenth anniversary and relive some of its greatest moments in the pages that follow.

Paul Lewis,
President and General Manager
Discovery Channel Canada

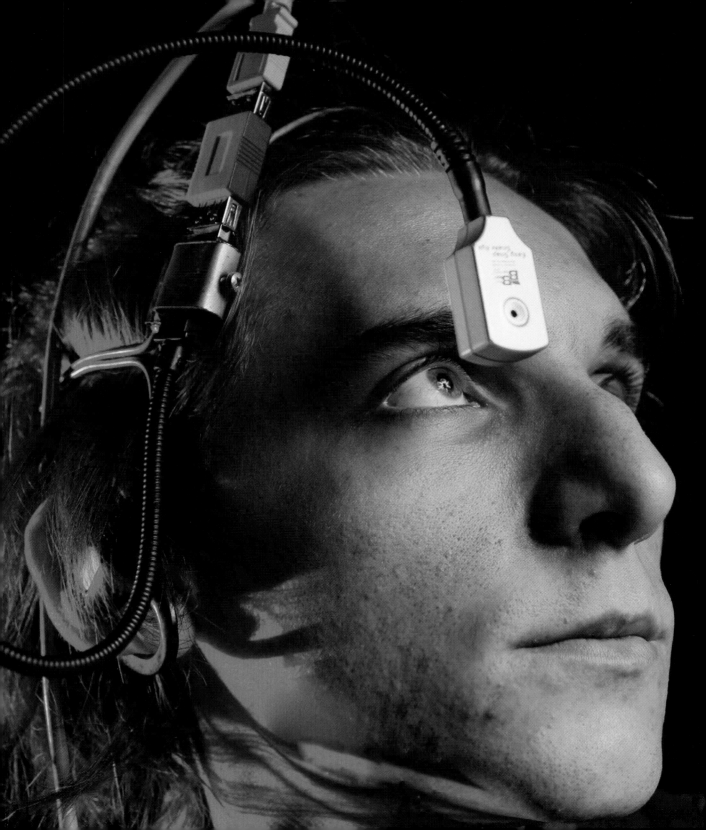

INTRODUCTION

AN ARTIST WHO "HEARS" COLOURS; A BICYCLE MADE OF BAMBOO; A BIRD that's half feathers, half model railroad car. Where else would you encounter a list as bizarre as this but on *Daily Planet*? Each is the product of ingenuity, imagination, and invention. Each is a response to a challenge, whether that is to understand a single species of bird better, to help an individual realize his potential, or even to provide a rational and sustainable form of transportation. In the beginning all such projects are simply ideas, with no material evidence for their existence—they're just notions or inspired guesses. That's the way science starts: researchers can imagine where they think the answers to their questions lie, and they can use ingenuity to invent ways of getting to them, but those answers are, at the beginning, only in their heads.

It's not just scientists who think and act that way: inventors, tinkerers, artists—they all do it. You don't have to have a Ph.D. to see challenges in nature that are just crying out to be met. Admittedly, challenges like building the world's lowest car or re-creating Stonehenge single-handedly are foreign to the kind of work going on in the science labs, but when it comes right down to it, they're all about the same kind of mental effort and creativity. At *Daily Planet* we look for anyone who has those qualities and has done something with them, whether they have the finest academic credentials or not.

It's a tribute to the creativity of the program's producers that I've been able (with plenty of help) to put together a collection of stories that are so different and yet have so much in common. Different because they range all over the planet, move easily from science to technology to engineering, and explore the world in every imaginable place at every conceivable scale. Much in common because each one represents someone, somewhere, who took up the quest and thought, worked, and created something new, whether that was a cloned sheep, the World Wide Web, or a robotic moose for catching poachers.

When you think about the underlying common features, it's clear that as you put together a set of stories about science and technology, you're assembling at the same time a remarkable group of people. So read on and meet them. Some, like Jane Goodall and Stephen Hawking, you'll already know. Many others you won't, but each has a story to tell.

Jay Ingram

ONE

Making Cool Things

Sometimes an invention makes people shake their heads and wonder why they didn't think of it; more often it makes people shake their heads in astonishment or even disbelief. But no matter where it takes place—the lab, the garage, or on someone's hard drive—an invention is the ultimate product of a fertile mind.

STONEHENGE RELOADED

◄ Wally Wallington and his concrete pillar: Stonehenge in Michigan.

MOST OF US HAVE SEEN PICTURES OF Stonehenge, the giant stone circle in the west of England. It's an amazing monument, not just for the size of its stones (many of which weigh more than 100,000 kilograms) or for its age (most of what we can see today was erected more than four thousand years ago), but for the combination of the two. How could people just emerging from the Stone Age move giant stones into place, then stand them up vertically? The seeming impossibility of the task has even prompted some to attribute it to the help of aliens, but there's a man in Flint, Michigan, with a much more prosaic explanation: some wood and some stones.

▶ Stonehenge ... after all the speculation, dubious theories, and intrigue, it's still awe-inspiring.

4

▲ Rope, wood, and ingenuity are all it takes to move 3.5 cubic metres of concrete.

His name is Wally Wallington, and he's a retired construction worker. Wally is convinced he's discovered how Stonehenge was made, and whether he's right or wrong about that monument, it's definitely true that he's figured out how to move huge weights with only the simplest of tools. For instance, a mere pebble placed under a concrete block weighing about as much as a minivan allows Wally to spin the block with apparent ease. Add a second pebble, rock the block from one end to the other, and rotate it at the same time, and he can start to walk the concrete block horizontally. But that's child's play compared to the task Wally set out for himself the day we visited him.

Wally had in front of him a single long block—8700 kilograms of concrete,

3.5 cubic metres of it—and he was going to try to stand it up, just like the stones at Stonehenge. It should be noted that in the late 1990s the American television program *Nova* tried to re-create raising a stone at Stonehenge, and this required a crowd of volunteers to lift it into vertical position. Wally's stone might have been smaller, but then, he was alone. And it wasn't as if he'd surrounded himself with the latest in heavy construction equipment.

"I'm trying to do this without any mechanical machinery at all," Wally explained. "I've used mostly sticks and stones for my equipment—no pulleys, no hoists, no metal levers. I just try to use gravity.... I believe that's my favourite tool."

We all experience gravity, but Wally *employs* it. First he had to raise the concrete block—still horizontal—up to a height of about a metre. That was easy: once the block was perched, teeter-totter-like, on a stack of wood that acted as the fulcrum, all Wally had to do was shift a set of weights to one end, and when the block tilted that way, insert a new piece of wood in the gap that was created. Then, the reverse: shift the weights, tilt the block in the other direction, insert another piece of wood. Gradually the block crept higher and higher, until it was ready. Wally described what he would do next:

The first thing I'm going to do here is release this temporary shoring I've set, then come over here and release some of my counterweights, and that's going

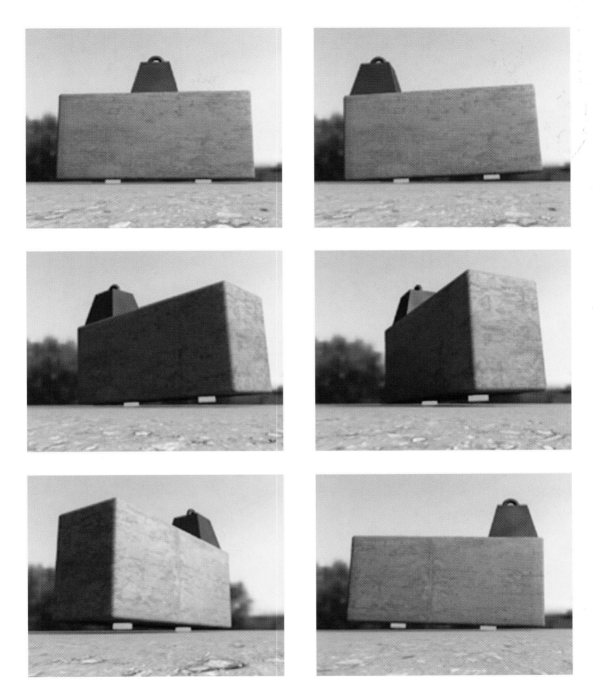

▲ As the weight slides from one end to the other, the concrete block tilts in response, and pieces of wood slid under it gradually raise it off the ground.

to put the entire weight of the block on this rope. So then I'm going to release the rope and the rope's going to be my brake. The easiest way I can explain this is that this is just a big teeter-totter, and I've got the big kid on that end, and he's going to go down and this end is goin' up.

And that's exactly what happened. The big kid went down, and the 8700-kilogram block stood up. To get it exactly perpendicular, Wally washed away sand from the walls of the pit to allow the block to continue to slide in.

Now, it's not completely fair to compare Wally's one-man show to other efforts to replicate Stonehenge, partly because true Stonehenge-scale stones are an ungodly weight four or five times that of Wally's block. Also, a true replication would require getting the stones from

▼ 8700 kilos slipping ...

where they were found to the site. There's controversy over just how far away some of Stonehenge's rock columns travelled, but it might have been tens of kilometres, something Wally didn't attempt. But hey, he's moved a barn 90 metres. Does anyone really think he couldn't move a stone across the countryside? Certainly Wally doesn't harbour any doubts: "If they were to use this technique to raise the stones at Stonehenge, I believe they could have gotten it down with a lot smaller crew than anybody has imagined."

He has some ideas about those Egyptians and their pyramids too. In the end, anyone can theorize about how ancient monuments were built, and many of those theories, perhaps understandably, underestimate the expertise that existed thousands of years ago. It's really all about ingenuity, not technology: just check out a backyard in Flint, Michigan, and you'll see what I mean.

▼ ... and sliding into the hole Wally dug for it.

PLACES WE'VE BEEN

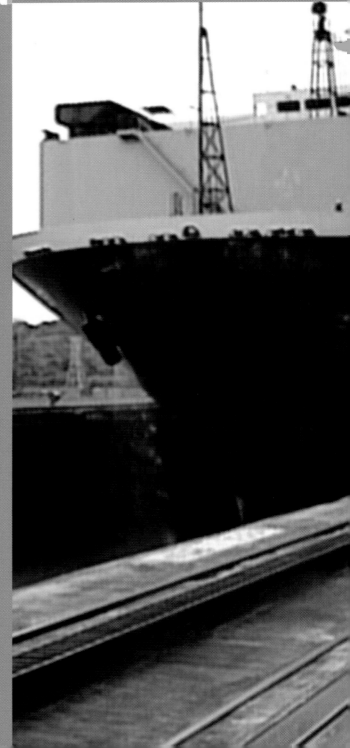

PANAMA CANAL

Watching the ships roll in …
then watch them roll away
again. The unceasing boat
traffic is the most striking thing
about the canal, and of course
the canal is what we all envision
when we think of Panama.
But in our brief time there we
climbed up a construction crane
to look down on the jungle
canopy, visited a refuge for
monkeys seized from private
owners, and stood by as
a government wildlife rescue
team "liberated" an ocelot
from a house in the suburbs.

ENGINEERING WITH HEART

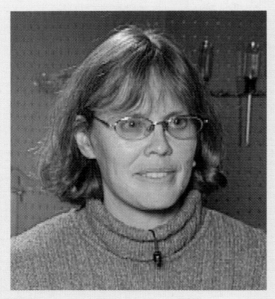

▲ Amy Smith, MIT engineer.

IN FEBRUARY 2010, *BUSINESSWEEK* magazine published its list of the "World's Most Influential Designers," and MIT engineer Amy Smith was on that list. This wasn't the first acknowledgment of her work: she also won a MacArthur "genius award" in 2004. Her genius is design and engineering, and here's what she had to say about it when we talked to her on *Daily Planet*:

> Engineering shouldn't be pushing the edge of technology for the top 5 percent of the world; engineering should be creating solutions for the 50 percent of the world who live on less than $2 a day and really need things to improve their daily lives.

And that's exactly what Amy Smith is busy doing. Her designs marry simplicity and ingenuity with necessity. Take her electric hammer mill—its simple job is to grind grain, something that in the developing world is often done by pounding the grain by hand with an outsized wooden tool, a scaled-up version of a mortar and pestle. It's been estimated that women around the world spend up to 20 *billion* hours a year grinding grain this way.

Hammer mills, so named because the grinding wheel, the fan, has small metal "hammers" attached to it, are a welcome substitute when they're working. But they have problems. Most of them use screens to separate the grain from the husks, which, if they're damaged, are hard to replace; they also have to be cleaned often because they get clogged. Amy's design is radically different: no screen necessary. The flour is caught in the airstream created by the rotating fan and is blown up out of the mill into a bag, while the chaff remains behind. Her hammer mill is also simpler, consumes less energy, and is cheaper.

This fertile mind hasn't stopped there. She's also devised simple plastic bags that decontaminate polluted water by exposing it to the ultraviolet light of the sun. In this case, it's not so much the idea (it's well known that UV light is antibacterial) as the execution. With a little folding and inside-out action, the bag can be filled and sealed, and a separate spout is created, then tucked back in. The bags are thin, ensuring complete penetration by the solar UV, so they're a clever double: water purifier and portable container.

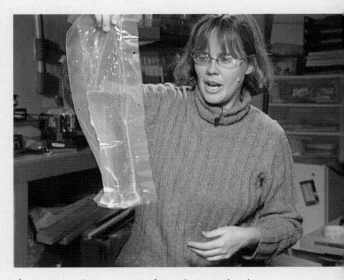

▲ UV-treated water … UV from the sun, that is.

▲ Sugar cane briquettes: a simple solution to a pressing environmental problem.

Amy Smith was also hard at work on solving environmental problems in Haiti long before the devastating earthquake. One of the many issues there was deforestation. So many trees had been felled for fuel that hillsides were denuded. No trees, no holding the soil back, and as a result hurricanes and heavy rainfalls were causing devastating floods. Amy realized that a wood substitute was needed, but most of the existing ones were either impractical or uneconomical. Haiti was, however, rich in leftover stalks from sugar-cane harvesting, but rather than burn them directly—an awkward and messy process at best—Amy and her students came up with the idea of turning the waste into charcoal by burning it in a big oil drum covered with a lid to exclude oxygen. Once the fibres were carbonized, the problem was finding something to bind them into briquettes. One of Amy's students remembered that as a kid he'd eaten porridge made from cassava, a local vegetable in Haiti. Gluey porridge. And Amy thought, "Perfect." The cassava worked, a press was adapted to squeeze the charcoal into discs, and sugar-cane briquettes were born.

Amy is too busy inventing to be worried that some might look askance at an MIT engineer who isn't creating the ultimate nanotechnology machine or a new-generation rocket fuel: "Coming up with something that's a really simple, effective way of solving problems is what engineering is all about. It doesn't have to be on the cutting edge, and it doesn't have to involve lasers and all the latest microprocessors."

One thing is true: this kind of engineering reaches deeply into the lives of the people who need it.

> "Coming up with something that's a really simple, effective way of solving problems is what engineering is all about. It doesn't have to be on the cutting edge, and it doesn't have to involve lasers and all the latest microprocessors."
> AMY SMITH

▲ Hammer mills aren't glamorous, but they're definitely making a difference.

THE FLATMOBILE IS ...

THE WORLD'S LOWEST CAR. ACTUALLY the world's lowest *roadworthy* car. That's lowest as in the car reaches only 19 inches (48 centimetres) above the ground, and there's only an inch (!) between the bottom of the car and the road.

What madness is this? Perry Watkins is the creator, but he's no more mad than many others we've encountered over the years who combine a nearly innate sense of engineering with a wild, independent streak. Perry has built peculiar cars before. One, called the Dalek, reminds me of the Badonkadonk (see page 42) but was actually modelled on the robotlike organisms from the *Doctor Who* series. Perry's Dalek apparently wasn't bent on universal conquest as the originals were, though it did have an unsettling effect on other drivers—they couldn't take their eyes off it. After all, it was 9 feet (2.7 metres) tall, with an eye in the front and a PA system that screamed, "You will be exterminated!"

But whereas the Dalek was truly outlandish and bizarre, the Flatmobile prompts a double take because it *is* just a car, in a way. Actually two cars: two Hillman Imps, parts of which are integrated into the final product. One advantage of the Imp was that it had a very compact engine, and in a Flatmobile, *compact* is the magic word. Perry lopped off everything above the tops of the doors, and shrank and flattened the suspension. Oddly enough, while he kept the original 5-gallon (18-litre) fuel tank under the hood, he loaded 70 kilos of lead onto it—otherwise the Flatmobile would have been so rear-heavy (with the engine in the back) that you could have picked up the front end of the car with one hand. The steering wheel is mounted on an extendable steering column: push it in and at least you can crawl into the car; pull it out and you can steer. If this all sounds fairly straightforward, even a little pedestrian, well, there's more, as Perry explains: "Behind the standard engine we have, of course, the gas-turbine jet engine, which is a home-built gas turbine producing about 150 pounds of thrust, which would probably add about another 50 miles per hour to the car's top speed."

It's "lowest" not "slowest," after all. If you're wondering why, when you're building the world's lowest car, you need to equip it with a jet engine, bear in mind that the Flatmobile is modelled quite faithfully on the 1960s Batmobile.

But looks aren't everything. This car has to be roadworthy to own the world record, and so driving it is necessary. And that's sometimes a little hazardous, according to Perry: "You're pretty much lying down in the car, very straight, very low; it's quite difficult to drive. You do have to keep your wits about you very much. Because it's only 19 inches tall it's lower than most people's garden walls, even their bedding plants in some cases, so people pulling out of a side road will look, and where they would normally see a car, you may be coming but they wouldn't see you."

And as if all that weren't enough: "If you're out and about in the car, the ground clearance is only one inch, so you do have to be on the lookout for speed bumps, dead animals, pheasants, rabbits, hedgehogs, Coke cans…."

▲ It's not them, it's the car: it's 19 inches high!

3-D JAY

IN THE FIFTEEN YEARS THAT *DAILY PLANET* has been on the air, my producers have asked me to go to all kinds of places and do some crazy things, but none more extreme than falling several storeys and getting crushed by a car. Fortunately, it wasn't a flesh-and-blood "me" in this stunt, but an uncannily accurate 3-D, virtual me.

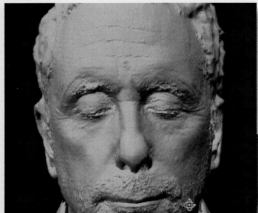

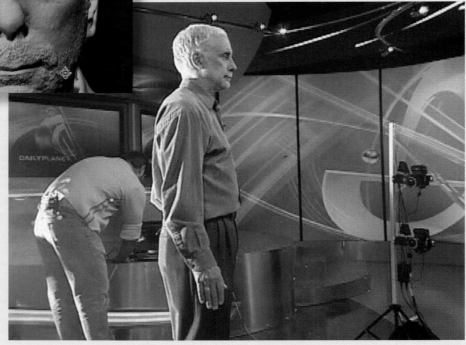

▲ Being scanned to create a lifelike replica.

Ottawa 3-D visual effects company XYZ RGB came to the *Daily Planet* studio to create my digital doppelgänger. I'd like to think this was a high point for them, but given that they've produced images for the *Matrix* movies, *King Kong, 300,* and *Blades of Glory,* well, maybe not. Jon Coulter and Helmut Kungl set their high-speed single-lens reflex cameras in a circle around me, and in less than 1/100th of a second, they had the information they needed to create my virtual body. To get the greater detail of my face, they projected a pattern of light on it and used that to extract higher-resolution 3-D information, taking thirty images in the same time as the body system took one.

The beauty of all this was that once they had the data to create the 3-D me in their computer system (or what they called my "three-dimensional essence"), they could make me do things that I might not be able to do myself. Actually, things that I absolutely couldn't do myself. But there are some people out there who can, and the trick is to record their body movements as they do something amazing, then map those onto a "skeleton" they'd created for me.

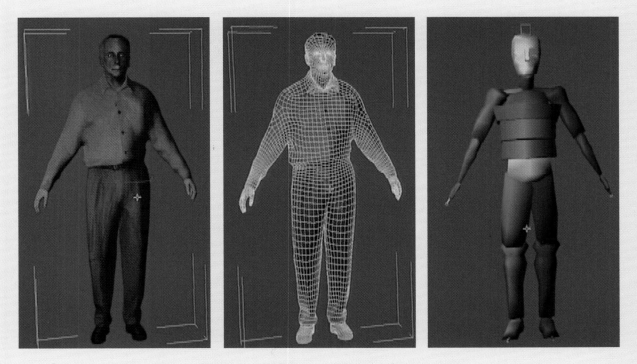

▲ One Jay, three looks: the artistry of the high-speed, single-lens reflex camera.

Once they'd done that, it was open season on Jay. Some of the action was flattering: there I was, lashing out with a vicious airborne kick to level an opponent. I admit I found it slightly disconcerting that my opponent was me! But the climax was my terrifying fall from a great height, being battered and bounced this way and that off a series of strategically placed wooden planks. As if that weren't enough, my prone body was then crushed by a falling car.

As devastating as that was, I knew that if John and Helmut had only bothered, my 3-D person could have shrugged off that car—and maybe even torn it in half.

▲ Mapping action onto a 3-D skeleton makes some stylish moves possible.

▶ Taking it like a man!

24

◀ ▲ Falling wasn't so bad, but getting crushed was a bit much.

TIM BERNERS-LEE,

INVENTOR OF THE WORLD WIDE WEB, ON WHY HE PASSED UP THE CHANCE TO BECOME RICH FROM THE WEB

"I have a reasonable salary, and I have a lot of fun and I'm in a great place to work. There are a lot of aspects to 'gain' other than monetary gain. If I had been of the mind to start a company and capitalize on it and license the technology—which I of course considered—then I would have done it fairly early on, and I don't think the Web would be where it is today.... I think there would have been competitors to the Web, and also we would not have the World Wide Web Consortium as a central coordinating body. So that was my decision at the time.... It's a frequently asked question ... but I've gotten a lot out of the Web."

A FLYING CAR?

OVER OUR FIFTEEN YEARS OF PROGRAM-ming we've talked many times about the "flying car," that as-yet-unrealized dream vehicle that you back out of the garage, then drive away—straight up! We've wanted a car that can fly for almost as long as we've had the automobile; James Bond, Harry Potter, and, of course, the Jetsons took them for granted. So some version of an airborne vehicle deserves a place in this book, but which one? We think the Carter Copter qualifies. It might not match your vision of a flying car, but as Jay Carter says, "the idea is to make this plane so simple and safe that the average person who can drive an automobile can fly this aircraft."

Jay Carter runs his own company, Carter Aviation Technologies, and his Carter Copter (which was the original prototype for what are now called PAVs: Personal Air Vehicles) is a vehicle of unusual design, one that blends innovation with tradition. The traditional part is that it is an autogyro, an aircraft with a free-spinning rotor that provides lift but doesn't contribute to its forward speed. Amelia Earhart flew an

▶ Jay Carter's four-person personal air vehicle.

▲ Carter envisioning the skies full of his PAVs.

Those jump takeoffs Jay Carter mentioned are the result of spinning up the rotor while it's horizontal, then tilting it forward; as the propeller kicks in the aircraft literally leaps off the ground. That cool concept demonstrates that Jay Carter is a creative guy; the testing of the rotor and the propeller shows that he also doesn't back down from a challenge. It requires that Carter sit inside the housing, a metre or so away from a blade that's spinning at the speed of sound:

> Notice we've got 6000 pounds of concrete on the sides here just to kinda help this from taking off … and then here, of course, is where I actually get in while we're doing the testing. We've got ⅜-inch-thick steel plate all around it and 2-inch tempered Plexiglas. So I sit in here and I look at the instruments. The armour is just in the event that something bad happens and a rotor blade comes off or we miss something. And that would be pretty intense.

autogyro, and in fact set a record in 1931 by flying it to 18,453 feet. The innovation part is that this aircraft could be the one that comes closest to becoming the first flying car.

> Basically our aircraft is a combination of fixed-wing aircraft with an autogyro. It has a propeller to provide forward thrust, but it also has a rotor and a wing. The rotor provides much of the lift for slow speed and jump takeoffs, but then when we get going fast, our wings start picking up more and more of the lift to the point where the wings can provide all of the lift, and at that point the rotor is just along for the ride.

So if this technology was around in the 1930s, why isn't it dominant today? Probably because those early autogyros couldn't do anything that either airplanes or the fledging helicopter couldn't already do. But things are different today. Jay Carter and his team are now developing a four-person craft called the 4-place PAV. When they finally have the composite material airframe ready, and they've tweaked the

▲ ▼ Carter-inspired aircraft might one day play many roles.

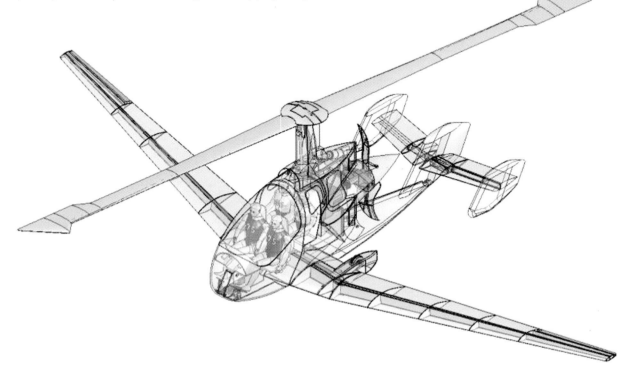

design, they want to demonstrate it around the globe, which also doesn't faze Jay Carter:

> Basically because this aircraft can fly so far, it's so efficient, that a world-wide demo tour for us is going to be an easy thing. We're only looking at four or five stops.

In the meantime companies in the aerospace business have been calling and coming by for tours, and Jay thinks that they're both intrigued and bewildered: "This is not a complementary technology to anything that they're doing. It's what they call a disruptive technology, in that it obsoletes what they've got." But they find it hard to ignore the potential: the Carter Copter could be scaled up to be a passenger airliner, military transport, or even an emergency aircraft. But we at *Daily Planet* don't really care about all those. We just want one in the garage, and Jay Carter doesn't disagree:

> There's no reason that this aircraft wouldn't cost as little as any other four-place automobile. Truly. It boils down to volume production and simplicity in design, and that's what we have.

▶ Jay Carter can imagine the day when this might not cost more than a mid-priced car.

BRIAN THE EAGLE

IT'S AN UNFORTUNATE TRUTH THAT SOMETIMES THE COMBINATION OF hard work, cool technology, and caring can't help people achieve exactly what they set out to do. Brian the bald eagle might be an example of that, but I'll leave it up to you to decide whether this is a success story or not.

▲ Brian could not have survived in the wild.

Brian was admitted to Vancouver Island's North Island Wildlife Recovery Centre in Errington, B.C., nearly ten years ago, in 2001. He'd been shot, and most of his upper bill had been blown away. Brian survived the gunshot, but the wound was profound, and the risk was that the rest of his upper bill would break off as he fed:

▲ Brian with one of his many prostheses.

eagles like to pull and tear away at their food, putting enormous pressure on the bill.

So a radical idea was born: give Brian a prosthesis, an add-on to his bill to protect what was left of the original. The idea was great; the execution, very, very tricky. Nanaimo dentist Brian Andrews (the eagle's namesake) and denturist Fred Leak created the first prosthesis, but it failed within a couple of weeks. From then on Fred was point man on the project. Because something like this had never been done before, he was operating in the dark, and he likely never expected that over the course of Brian's life, he would have to create *ten* different prostheses.

The add-ons were made of orthodontic acrylic, the same stuff used for retainers that keep teeth in place once they've been shifted around by braces. The prosthesis was light and pretty strong, but the challenge was attaching it to what was left of

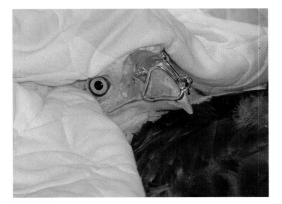

▲ The fearsome predator tucked in his blankie.

▲ Ten different versions of Brian's prosthesis were made.

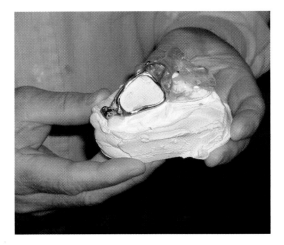

▲ This project pushed the limits of orthodontics.

Brian's bill. It couldn't be glued, because if something got caught between the acrylic and the bill, there would be no way to remove it. For that reason, the dental team merely anchored the first prosthesis to the rest of Brian's bill with a tiny screw. But the pressure created when Brian ate—like an eagle—was too much, and the artificial bill failed.

Fred worked on extending the add-on to cover more of the bill, but then a new problem surfaced: even though a nostril had been incorporated into the prosthesis, moisture from the eagle's breath became trapped between the plastic and the bill itself, and the bill began to soften and rot. It was like leaving your thumbnail (which is made of the same protein, keratin) in water for a week. About half a millimetre of surface structure of the beak was lost,

meaning that new models had to be resized and designed to allow for that.

Back to the drawing board. This time Fred rebuilt the prosthesis with a metal frame that allowed it to breathe. This seemed to solve the moisture problem, but even so, Fred had to replace the device about once a year, and at every step of the way he encountered tiny details that he had to take into account. For one thing, there are two tiny, fleshy prongs on an eagle's tongue that help move food down its gullet—Fred had to be careful that his prosthesis didn't interfere with those. And even then new problems arose: eventually Brian's bill began to twist to one side, and Fred tried to straighten it using the same techniques that allow braces to straighten teeth.

In the end the prosthesis had become too cumbersome for Brian, so it was removed, and he was fed cut-up meat by one of the staff at the Wildlife Recovery Centre. But he was losing weight and getting weaker, and finally Brian the eagle was euthanized on March 7, 2009.

Success or failure? Brian wouldn't have survived for more than a few days or weeks in the wild, so his years at the Wildlife Recovery Centre were a bonus. But despite Fred Leak's efforts, a perfect prosthesis never resulted. Even so, along the way Fred learned a lot about the subtle engineering of that bill, and he has been asked to consult with other institutions about injured birds in their care.

Perhaps most important, Brian became famous, and the publicity surrounding him and the efforts to help him probably shone more light on the cruelty and irresponsibility of illegal eagle hunting than anything else could have.

▲ Brian with Robin Campbell, wildlife manager at the North Island Wildlife Recovery Association.

WHY RECYCLE WHEN YOU CAN REINVENT?

THE FIRST TIME WE MET JIM MEANEY he was ordering the hot turkey sandwich in his sister's café in Bay Roberts, Newfoundland. Jim was careful to make sure the pop that came with the sandwich was in a can. This is the same Jim Meaney who, when he sees the soft drink delivery guy coming in with a cart loaded with ten flats of pop cans, thinks, "There goes another solar panel!"

No wonder Jim is a little hyper when a pop can catches his eye—those cans are the guts of his prime invention, the Cansolair, an ingenious device for using solar energy to heat buildings. It would be nice to say this is another rags-to-riches story, but it hasn't been an easy go for Jim; it's more of a rags-to-riches-back-to-rags-then-maybe-more-riches

◀ A Cansolair panel: simple.

sort of thing. But it all starts with a man who has an indefinable knack for creating mechanical devices, for assembling things that never wanted to be assembled: "I'm the kind of guy who walks into a room, or a shed, looks at all the junk, and it just clicks, you know?"

It clicked when, as a kid, Jim built a tricycle with wheelbarrow tires and a 14-horsepower engine. And it clicked when life's everyday challenges forced him to contemplate sustainable energy: "I found out firsthand what it was like to be newly married and trying to raise kids and pay bills and having your power cut because you couldn't pay your utility bills. The wind was blowing, the sun was shining, and again, being a mechanic, all that got me thinking."

But invention, at least in the beginning, often staggers and stumbles around a bit, and that's what happened to Jim. With, as he says, "too much time on my hands," he started fooling around with stacking pop cans, drilling holes in their lids and bottoms, and forcing warm air through them with a hair dryer, all of which soon showed him that aluminum cans were pretty good at giving up any heat that entered them. But the airflow wasn't adequate until Jim tried out a pair of snips and created the equivalent of vanes in the ends of the cans.

Here's the current version of his inspiration, the Cansolair. Pop and beer cans are recovered from the recycling depot (even that first step saves energy, because the city doesn't have to crush them and melt

▼ Jim Meaney, likely planning his next invention.

▼ Vanes cut into the ends of the cans improve the flow of hot air.

them down). For each Cansolair panel, 240 cans are cleaned, the lids and bottoms are snipped, and the cans are arranged in a frame and painted with fine black paint to enhance absorption of solar energy. Then the frame is sealed with a tough, weather-resistant, transparent polycarbonate cover. The cans are definitely low-tech; the cover, not so much. "That stuff is practically bullet-proof," Jim says. "I think sandwiched between two panes of glass, it'll stop a rifle bullet point-blank."

Once the Cansolair is installed on a roof or an outside wall, a fan draws cool air into one end of the unit, and warm air flows out the other end. Jim has sold thousands of units, and while they can't provide 100 percent of the heat for your house, they don't cost an arm and a leg either. They're simple, easily maintained, and, when you consider that the raw materials are reused and the energy comes from the sun, elegant.

But Jim's business isn't out of the woods yet; a variety of issues have plagued him and made it difficult to keep up production. Still, the orders keep coming in. And he has, like all true inventors, a host of other ideas that he hopes one day will attract some serious interest, research, and even funding. He's a guy who lives with uncertainty, success, and failure, apparently in roughly equal measures:

"It has been a rollercoaster ride all right, like when I tied my parasail to the bumper of my truck, but it's an adventure I wouldn't miss for the world. Wish me luck."

▼ Once the cans are laid end to end ...

▼ ... they're painted black to absorb solar radiation more efficiently.

THE BADONKADONK

AS WE SO MEMORABLY SAID AT THE TIME we presented the Badonkadonk to viewing audiences across Canada, "It was created to fill the demand for a land battle tank/party vehicle."

The Badonkadonk, or "Donk" for short, is definitely one of the top five in *Daily Planet*'s long history of technology run amok, venturing so far off the beaten path that its chances of finding the path again are, well, zero. Neal Ormond is the inventor and a former Stanford University marching band drummer. The latter occupation doesn't explain his inventing style, which he describes as "no bounds in genres or styles, as long as it's crazy and different."

And as for calling his creation the Badonkadonk, otherwise a slang term for a big butt?

"We were watching TV one night after working on the Donk all day and someone quoted that

▶ When you first see it, you don't know whether to cheer or run for your life.

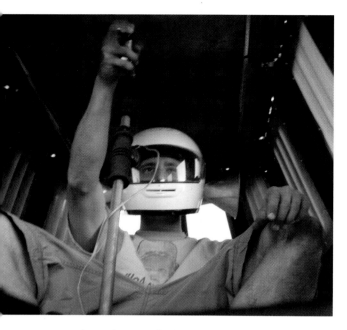

▲ Neal Ormond tells us it's "road-legal."

necessary headlights and brake lights in case, as Neal says, "you get pulled over—it could happen in a vehicle like this."

But it's not all functional. Actually very little of it is. Passengers can enjoy an open-air ride as well, clustered along the roof rail, and music is heard loud and clear no matter where you're placed in the Donk. Most important, Neal is fond of propane and the flame it generates, so the Donk is loaded with pyrotechnics, including rocket pods (actually not rockets but noisy electric arcs) and a "ring of fire" around the roofline.

It serves Neal's self-described urge to be "crazy and different," but the Donk isn't all he's come up with. While we were there taking in the Donk, Neal took time out to reveal the Pneumatipak II, an all-purpose, all-ammunition cannon. It shoots hot dogs, C batteries, anything that can fit down the barrel. Of course there's also the liquid reservoir that can be attached, making it possible to shoot water, paint, or beer. It's all powered by a backpack cylinder of carbon dioxide. Neal took a moment to fire a helpless carrot into the dead tree in his backyard to demo the ruthless power of the Pneumatipak II.

Were we surprised by the sudden appearance of a carrot-shooting cannon? No. When you're in Neal Ormond's backyard, it pays to remember his motto: "If it's something that's ordinary and everyday, it holds no interest for me. I'd rather do something that's going to make people just step back and say, 'What the heck?!'"

line, said something about a 'badonkadonk butt,' and we hadn't heard the word before, but obviously right then it pretty much exactly described the vehicle that we were building out back."

How to describe the Donk? At first glance the sheet metal surface suggests a miniature land version of some centuries-old ironclad ship, with Neal, as captain, *standing up* while driving it. Standing up, that is, with head and shoulders exposed. This is possible because steering and braking are handled by a joystick, with acceleration controlled by a foot pedal. It does look retro, but it also hints at a hovercraft, because the skirt of the Donk hides the wheels. All the same, it does have the

◀ The Donk is fully equipped for nighttime adventures as well.

▼ A brilliant pyrotechnic display: the Donk demonstrates its rooftop "ring of fire."

PLACES WE'VE BEEN

JAPAN

In Japan we experienced everything from the intense humanity of Tokyo's Shibuya Square to the hillsides of Arashiyama, where macaque monkeys are in charge. But perhaps the most striking contrasts were those between real life (the monkeys and the chimps at the Primate Research Institute at Kyoto University) and robots. We saw snake-like robots that can roll or crawl over obstacles, robots that can discern emotional differences in human speech and respond accordingly, and of course the Japanese specialty: uncanny (even slightly disturbing) humanoid robots.

TWO Outliers

In statistics, outliers are numbers that sit apart from most of the other numbers in a group. They attract the attention of skeptical statisticians. But outliers can also be people who see things a little differently than the rest and act on those insights. They attract attention too, but for all the right reasons.

"I'VE BEEN COLD MANY, MANY TIMES"

FEW SIGHTS ON TELEVISION ARE MORE alarming than seeing a snowmobile with two men aboard plunge through the ice into freezing cold, open water. And while it might lessen the thrill to know that a camera crew and rescuers wait nearby, that very fact heightens the amazement: these guys did that for our entertainment?!

Well, no, not for our entertainment, but to grab our attention for an important message: hypothermia is a threat, and preparing for it can save your life.

Dr. Gordon Giesbrecht runs the Laboratory for Exercise and Environmental Medicine at the University of Manitoba in Winnipeg. But he's much more than a lab administrator; Gordon is always ready to put himself in hazardous situations—circumstances that challenge survival. He has been hypothermic more than thirty times, and he was once again for *Daily Planet*.

▲ ▶ You wouldn't do something like this unless you knew exactly what you were in for.

Getting back on solid ice is only the first step in surviving such an accident. But it's obviously a crucial one, and, as Dr. Giesbrecht pointed out, there's a smart way of doing it: swim back in the direction you came from, because at least you know you'll find solid ice there. Even if the ice ahead of you is closer and *looks* solid, you can't be sure it's safe. Death from drowning may be an even greater risk than hypothermia: you could probably stay in the water for fifteen minutes before hypothermia kicked in. Even with mild hypothermia, that is, when your core body temperature is in the range of 32 to 35 degrees Celsius (normal is 37), you can still function. However, lower temperatures than that begin to cloud your thinking and your ability to shiver to warm your muscles. At this point your life is in danger.

◀ Hauling yourself out onto the ice is the first step.

▼ Crawling to safety may take a very long time.

52

Ironically, Dr. Giesbrecht found that the cold shock he expected, the hyperventilation and gasping you see in the lab when someone in a bathing suit is plunged into water at 2 degrees Celsius, just didn't happen to him. Maybe cold shock isn't all that common in the real world. But it would be a terrible mistake to think that once you're out of the water, you're safe. Depending on where you are, getting onto the ice is only the first step: yes, you've dodged one bullet, but hypothermia is still stalking you, and now getting warm and staying that way become all-important. As far as Dr. Giesbrecht is concerned, making a fire is number one: "If you absolutely couldn't light a fire, you're in a dire, dire situation. If you just sit there with your wet clothes on, you might survive the first night, but if you're not found, you're certainly not going to survive the second night."

Making that fire, drying your clothes, building a lean-to for shelter overnight, and eventually lighting a signal fire are all steps that you must be prepared for. After all, isn't that what survival is all about: preparation? Dr. Giesbrecht's nighttime dunking highlighted that fact. He wore a standard snowmobile suit, designed for comfort and warmth, but his companion had taken the precaution of donning a flotation suit, made of the same stuff as life jackets—a little more restrictive, but a whole lot safer if you find yourself in ice-cold water.

Even if the ice ahead of you is closer and *looks* solid, you can't be sure it's safe. Death from drowning may be an even greater risk than hypothermia: you could probably stay in the water for fifteen minutes before hypothermia kicked in. However, lower temperatures than 32 to 35°C begin to cloud your thinking and your ability to shiver to warm your muscles. At this point your life is in danger.

Once in the water, both headed back toward the ice they'd just been riding on, but their progress was dramatically different. Giesbrecht's partner in the flotation suit managed to swim the 90 metres to solid ice in about ten minutes, but Dr. Giesbrecht actually made little or no progress at all. His snowmobile suit was the culprit, he says: "The biggest problem was the effect of cold sapping all the energy out of your body, compounded by the fact that having at least 60 to 80 pounds of water in the suit [30 litres or more] made it virtually impossible to swim."

He couldn't lift his arms or even maintain a horizontal body position in order to backstroke his way to safety, and when he was pulled out of the water, he knew that, without help, he might have lasted only another minute or so. He recalls, "I got to the point where I realized that there's no way I'm going to make it to the ice. I could really only swim here for a couple more minutes, probably thirty seconds."

He managed to "swim" a mere 15 metres in six minutes of desperate effort. The point here is that it's likely not hypothermia that will kill you. You'd be more likely to drown by sucking in water as you gasped with effort or by getting trapped under the ice. In this case a rescue boat waited nearby, so Dr. Giesbrecht's peril seemed worse than it really was. But if you're tempted to think that this was just another phony television moment, think again. As Dr. Giesbrecht explains, his experience was very real:

For one brief moment I kinda shut everything else out, shut the lights out, the fact that there were rescue people behind me, and just tried to put myself in the place of a victim, as if this was for real. And it was an amazing moment, just a feeling of total isolation and desperation and helplessness. Just realizing that if this *was* for real, this would be a really lousy way to die. Because it's not quick—you have time to think about it.

▲ Dr. Gordon Giesbrecht put his life on the line by taking the plunge—literally—for *Daily Planet*.

THE GOD MACHINE

TRAVELLING AND INTERVIEWING WITH *DAILY PLANET,* I'VE MET A lot of pretty cool, smart, and fascinating people. But one of my most memorable experiences involved some individuals I *didn't* meet. They didn't show up when they were supposed to—and it was entirely my fault.

This all took place at Laurentian University in Sudbury, Ontario, in one of the eeriest lab setups I've ever seen. Dr. Michael Persinger is a neuroscientist there, and for years he's been investigating experiences that are far off the beaten track, at least from the scientific point of view. One is the near-death experience; another, alien abduction, or its less controversial cousin, the feeling of a presence.

Dr. Persinger became convinced that these phenomena were simply the result of certain unusual patterns of brain activity, and he created an experimental environment to test that hypothesis. The experiment consisted of stimulating the right hemisphere of volunteers' brains with weak magnetic fields, the idea being that some individuals are predisposed to react to such disturbances, which Dr. Persinger likened to waking dreams, by feeling that a mysterious presence is in the room with them. Of course, I wanted to meet those mystery people, or aliens, so up to Sudbury I went.

The lab was split in two: in the control room Dr. Persinger and his students generated and controlled the magnetic fields, while I was to sit in the adjoining soundproof room, "the chamber," in what I described at the time as a "battered, shabby, 50s-era easy chair." But the details of the room weren't important because as long as I was in there, I was going to be in a state of sensory deprivation: blind-folded and helmeted, with electrodes recording my brain activity and magnetic fields pulsing into my right hemisphere. Those magnetic fields were extremely weak, but sufficient, at least with the right subjects, to induce what Dr. Persinger called "intense, apprehensive, dream-like conditions."

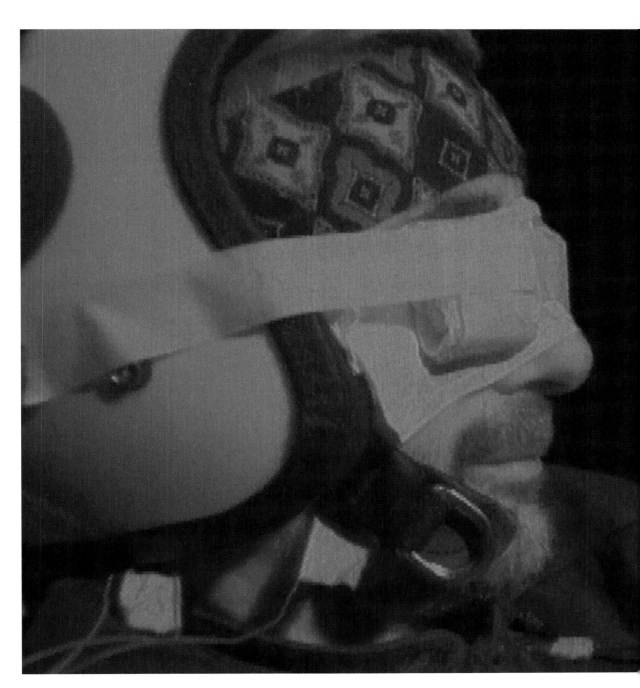

▲ With a blindfold, helmet, and easy chair, complete sensory deprivation never felt so comfortable—or looked so strange.

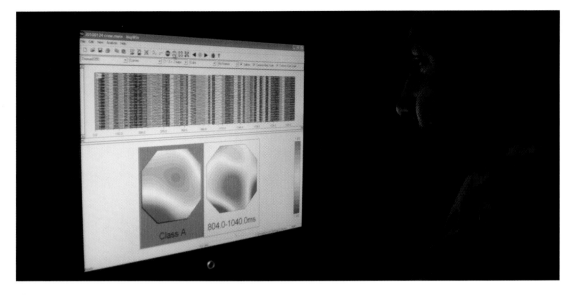

▲ Some people's brains react to magnetic fields in the strangest way.

He was pretty confident that, with a significant percentage of the population he tested, something dramatic happens: "It has to do with the sense of self—what we call the 'sense of self' is primarily a left-hemispheric language process. The equivalent process in the right hemisphere, which we're typically not aware of, is the source of the visitation experience. And when this right-hemispheric equivalent of the sense of self intrudes into awareness, you have the feeling of a presence." This idea isn't without controversy. But while neuroscientists might not agree about the exact mechanism, all *do* agree that the brain is where it takes place.

But was I the right subject? In the preliminary phase I had to fill out a questionnaire to determine if I was stable enough—not prone to seizures or any extreme psycho-logical reaction—to go through with the experiment. But at the same time, the questionnaire might have revealed that I was so stable as to be unlikely to experience an unscheduled caller.

I'll say one thing: it was a peaceful experience. I had no sense of any magnetic fields or anything being pulsed through my brain, and in fact I pretty much lost contact with the rest of the world. But no "other" dropped in to see me. The best I could manage was the occasional miniature white face that popped up before my (closed) eyes, but if I dared turn my attention toward those faces, they winked out. They didn't speak, they didn't even seem to be looking at me, and they were more mask-like than real. And that was that. Apparently I had done a little too well on the pre-test:

"Judging from your test you have a very stable profile; you're a very stable personality. You'd be in the average range. It's highly imaginative individuals, writers, musicians, who are the ones that, with a single stimulation, feel the sense of presence. It's about 30 percent of individuals like this, who are slightly elevated on the temporal lobe sensitivity spectrum, who will experience a sense of presence, a feeling of thoughts coming from outside their own brain."

So I left Dr. Persinger's lab somewhat disappointed: no alien presence, not creative enough. I will say this for myself: maybe I didn't fall into that "highly imaginative" group, but I sure took up a lot of videotape describing how I didn't really see anything. That's creativity of a sort.

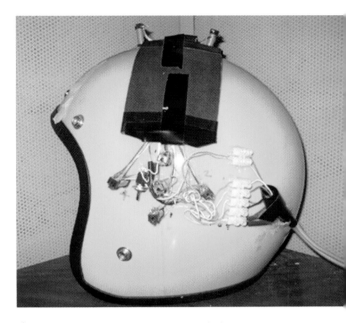

▲ Magnetic fields surge through the helmet, stimulating the brain's right hemisphere.

◀ No alien presence. Perhaps the shabby 50s-era easy chair was too comfortable?

IAN WILMUT,

ONE OF THE TEAM THAT CLONED THE FIRST ANIMAL, DOLLY THE SHEEP, IN 1996

"Quite a number of years ago now there were people working with embryos from amphibians, and they found that if you took cells from the skin of adult frogs and did nuclear transfer from them, they were able to develop to the tadpole stage. In actual fact none of these ever became adults. We think that this lamb is the first offspring to complete its whole development and come to term....

"It's genetically identical to the ewe from which we took the genetic material, but not an exact copy: as you know, even with identical twin humans, they are very, very, very similar, but there are small differences between them because of differences in the way the fetuses develop. There are a number of ethical questions with this research, and one of them is that human beings are of course mammals, and sometime in the future someone might want to clone a human. But as far as we're concerned we can see no clinical reason why you would wish to copy a human being."

Dolly died in 2003. No human has yet been cloned.

1/144TH OF WORLD WAR II

THERE'S SOMETHING BOTH PUZZLING and engaging about hobbyists. Puzzling because if you're not one of them you may find it impossible to understand why someone would build a replica of the Great Northern Railroad's switching yard in his (and it's mostly *his*) basement, but engaging because that person exhibits such traits as attention to detail, patience, love of authenticity, and plain hard work that we admire in inventors and scientists.

We at *Daily Planet* have a particular fondness for such people, because they prove that innovation and invention are not limited to the labs, but happen every day in backyards and garages around the world (see "Cansolair," page 38, and "Stonehenge Reloaded," page 4).

So it was that we journeyed to Texas to take in an epic naval confrontation—in miniature. On the shore of a man-made

▶ The battle is epic. The scale? Well, smallish.

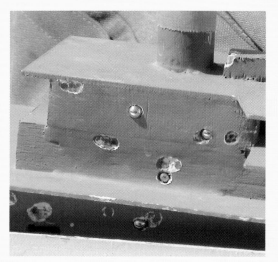

lake, the North Texas Battle Group gathered for the latest in their scaled-down reruns of World War II sea battles. On this day, the French battleship *Dunkerque* and the Italian *Andrea Doria* were teaming up to attack an Allied convoy protected by a battleship, the USS *Missouri,* and the heavy

◀ This battered bridge has taken several direct hits from ball-bearing artillery.

▼ Naval warfare at 1/144th scale happens by remote control.

cruiser USS *Dallas.* When we arrived the guys were just preparing their ships for the battle. Jeff Burns, captain of the *Dallas,* freely admitted, "I've got an ugly ship. The fine detail work has a tendency to get knocked off. So over time we put some of that back on, but since it's not necessary to the combat operation of the ship, a lot of times it just gets left off, so over time she gets to be a much uglier ship."

Jeff's comment that the fine detail work of his ship has been "knocked off" is a clue to the fact that this is no virtual battle—this is the real thing, albeit at 1/144th scale. These ships are built to exacting detail, including real guns, firing ball bearings with a muzzle velocity of 50 metres a second, 180 kilometres an hour. Small canisters of carbon dioxide provide the propulsive force. The steel balls don't just do the superficial damage

▼ Built to exacting detail, these ships could very well be in the North Atlantic.

The ships are controlled by standard radio frequency remote-control devices that manoeuvre the vessels, aim the guns, and fire the shots.

that causes the wear, tear, and uglification (although part of the disfigurement does consist of ball bearings still embedded in the hull); any ship that suffers a critical number of direct hits will sink. That's why Wes Wynne, captain of the *Dunkerque,* loaded a float into his ship before the battle. It would ensure that if his ship were to be sunk, he could recover the hull—the balsa wood superstructure would float on its own. It turned out he would need it.

In today's showdown, a convoy of tankers and cargo ships is sheltered in a harbour on one side of a boathouse. They must sail out and around a marker buoy, protected by the *Missouri* and the *Dallas,* then return to harbour. The *Dunkerque* and the *Andrea Doria* must try to sink them. The ships are controlled by standard radio frequency remote-control devices that manoeuvre the vessels, aim the guns, and fire the shots. But that makes it all sound a lot simpler than it really is.

You won't hold on to that misconception for long if you visit https://ntxbg.org, home port of the North Texas Battle Group. There, among posts like "Reviving electric motors that have been waterlogged one too many times" and "Skinning the hull, decks and superstructure," is a contribution by Jeff Burns, he of the ugly ship, emphasizing the importance of subtlety in convoying:

"Gunnery for a warship on convoy patrol [functions] more as a deterrence. Basically just to give the enemy something to think about. If it slows down an attacking warship, or causes it to back off, then the job is done. Many times just keeping the turrets tracking the attacking warship (without firing) is enough to give them a bit of a pause and cause at least a subtle change of tactics. That's generally enough to get another several feet towards the goal of a convoy run without new damage. As long as the attacking warship's captain thinks someone is alive at the gunnery position, many times the job is done for keeping the convoy afloat and underway.... If a convoy ship falls out of formation and gets pounced on? Leave it. Better to have one badly mauled or sunk convoy vessel than adding a warship into it and leaving other ships of the convoy undefended. Besides, the enemy's time spent dispatching a rogue transport is time very well spent for your convoy getting around the pond otherwise uncontested. Nothing like a bit of chum thrown well away from your position to distract/preoccupy the sharks."

Whether the captains of the *Missouri* and the *Dallas* read that post or not, they executed their convoy perfectly this day, and Wes and the *Dunkerque* were their primary victims. Wes's companion ship, the *Andrea Doria*, lost her guns, and his *Dunkerque* took several shots below the waterline. When the pumps failed, the ship took on water, until finally, painfully, she went down.

"The servo got wet, started glitching, and that caused the whole radio system to start glitching, and resulted in a loss of power with the *Dunkerque*, and loss of control. I tell you what: *Missouri* got in some gooooood hits."

But of course the *Dunkerque*, with a little tabletop repair, will live to fight again, and the only conceivable loss of life in this naval battle might have been some air-breathing insect stowaway that found itself going down with the ship.

▲ The ship went down, but all hands are safe.

APULANTA

HENNA HÄMÄLÄINEN WORKS FOR THE FINNISH INSTITUTE OF Occupational Health. She evaluates the physical and mental stress involved in a range of jobs, from soldiers to CEOs to chefs. But when *Daily Planet* caught up with her, she was going to a rock concert. Finland's biggest rock band, Apulanta, was the lead act, but Henna wasn't going to listen to them—she was going to *test* them.

You might not think of rock musician as a job: it seems so much more glamorous than that. But from Henna's point of view, a job is exactly what it is, even though the band might be on stage for only an hour. And Henna takes *her* job seriously: "The baseline measurements of the guys showed that their fitness level is better than if I just took someone off the street—they're not athletes, but their fitness level is quite high."

Baseline measurements enable Henna to put concert measurements into context, and that's why she's at this gig. She is nothing if not thorough: as they play she'll track heart rate, skin temperature, levels of the stress hormone cortisol, and, oh yes, *internal* body temperature. There's a pill for the band members to swallow that wirelessly transmits core body temperature readings, but Henna doesn't completely

▶ Toni, Sipe, and Sami: rock musicians and experimental guinea pigs.

▲ Is it just me, or is Sipe viewing that probe in Henna's hand with suspicion?

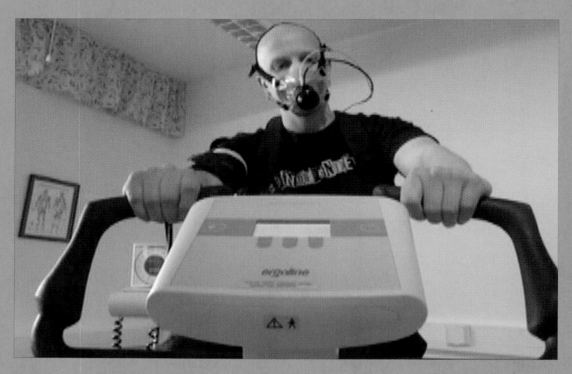

▲ Rock music is hard work, comparable to boxing or ditch-digging.

▲ Concert's over, data's collected.

trust the pill, so the guys—Toni, Sipe, and Sami—are in for a more traditional technology for measuring body temperature: the rectal probe. Henna describes it (with tongue in cheek) as "the best part." But they're rockers, and undaunted by 10 centimetres of scientific instrument. As he disappears into the washroom for a "fitting," Tony laughs: "Me and Mr. Probe here, we have some personal business to attend to."

Once they're onstage, Henna's point is proven: this is hard work. The band's physical exertion compares to moving furniture, boxing, digging ditches, and car racing. Body temperatures rise a full degree Celsius in sixty minutes, a dramatic change. And it's not just Henna who's intrigued by the results. "It's actually confirmed some things that we already knew," Tony explains, "but heart rates going up to 180 beats per minute? That's damn high actually, and that was surprising. The amount of calories that we burn in a show is quite astonishing, it's something like 800."

Rock band: it's a tough job, but you know what they say: someone has to do it.

JEARL WALKER

▲ Jearl Walker: meticulous researcher, pasta chef, and scientific daredevil.

PHYSICIST JEARL WALKER AND I GO back a long way, even to my radio days, and I've never met anyone who's more dedicated to his work. For all his protests that he's just a good ol' Texas boy, he's probably the most meticulous researcher I've ever known. When Jearl says something, it's likely true, especially if it's science. (Of course, much of the rest of it is bull.)

But Jearl also appreciates that vivid demonstrations beat simple explanations every time. Here are three of them.

Molten Lead

For this demonstration Jearl heated a pot of lead until it melted at about 300 degrees Celsius. Then, while explaining just how many things could go wrong, he vowed to plunge his bare hand into the molten lead—quickly—and withdraw it before he was burned.

It's possible to do this if you dip your hand in water first, because the thin layer of water on your hand will vaporize instantly

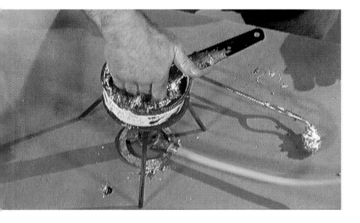

◀ Yes, that is molten lead that Jearl's hand is immersed in.

on contact with the lead, protecting your hand with a layer of steam—but just for a moment. Any hesitation and you're lost. Molten lead will cling to your hand and burn you severely.

Another risk, Jearl pointed out, was that the lead will solidify anyway, even if you're quick, if it isn't well over 300 degrees. Naturally he didn't have a thermometer with him, so he was really just guessing about the temperature. Well, not exactly guessing. He thrust a "volunteer" wiener into the lead, and it flapped back and forth, sustaining a serious burn. I guess that convinced Jearl that he could go ahead.

After mentioning one more risk, the container of molten lead spilling all over the table and us, he paused, plunged his hand in and out so quickly you could hardly follow it, and escaped unscathed. Wow! He has done this several times, but he has hurt himself doing it too; there was a nice description of once "watching the flesh melt away on my arm." The stills capture the moment beautifully.

Cornstarch

As Jearl carefully explained, water and cornstarch together form a *thixotropic fluid,* that is, the mixture behaves like a liquid when there are no stresses on it, but if you suddenly stress it, it becomes rigid like a solid. So there we were in the studio, giant mixing bowl with lots of water in front of us, Jearl shaking in what seemed like

▲ "If I were to suddenly stretch it, like THIS!"

pounds of cornstarch and stirring it around casually with his hand. Of course, he had no real idea of how much cornstarch to put in to reach that critical Jekyll and Hyde moment. So, while the cornstarch was still swirling from his stirring, he said, "If I were to suddenly stretch it, like THIS," and slammed his palm on the mixture, splashing it all over himself, and, as I soon realized was the whole point of the demonstration, all over me too.

Spaghetti

Jearl is from Texas and likes to attribute any of his flaws (in those rare moments when he admits to them) to that. So, for instance, when I asked him why he likes to eat spaghetti by taking one end of a strand in his mouth and slurping hard, he said, "In Texas, we don't use forks. We use hands. It's tradition, like barbecue." But he did add that there's some pretty crazy physics going on too. And he was right.

Here's the story. When you take just the tip of a strand of spaghetti in your mouth and suck, there will always be some wiggling or waving or whatever going on, and likely waves of motion rolling up and down the strand. That's no problem when most of the strand is hanging free—there's lots of spaghetti over which to spread the waves. But as the spaghetti disappears inside your pursed lips, while there's still a significant amount of energy being applied to the strand, less and less of it is outside your mouth and free to absorb those motions. The waves travelling up and down the spaghetti become more and more violent, and if you're lucky, the last wave will cause what's left of the spaghetti to smack into your face.

Try visiting Jearl's Flying Circus of Physics website (www.theflyingcircusofphysics.com). The science is fantastic. The research exhaustive. The humour? Well, Texan.

▲ Pasta—the Texas way.

AUSTRALIA

"Jay, the closer you sit to the edge of that cliff, the better the shot!" When *Daily Planet* travels to a country to feature the science and technology there, there are usually two different trips: one by producers to shoot the actual stories, and another with hosts to record intros and other links for the finished product. In this case we wanted to capture the wild beauty of Australia, and sitting on the edge of a cliff at North Head seemed like a good idea—at least to the producer and the cameraman.

THREE

Material World

The uniqueness of an object
may lie in its design, its
purpose, or even the
stuff from which it's made.
That stuff might be so radically new
("space-age material") that it alone sets the object apart.
But more interesting are familiar materials used in
unusual ways—or seen in a whole new light.

METAL IS SO TWENTIETH CENTURY

IF YOU CAN BUILD A SUPERCAR OUT OF WOOD, why stop there? Admittedly, a wooden diesel locomotive might be challenging, and aircraft stopped being wood-friendly as soon as they became jet powered, but there's one mode of transportation that just screams, "Make me out of wood!" The bicycle.

◀ This bicycle may be made of bamboo, but it's anything but crude.

The very first bicycles, in the early nineteenth century, were made almost entirely out of wood, and now, bike maker Craig Calfee in California has taken that as inspiration. Not only has he turned the clock back by rejecting metal in favour of an organic substitute, but he's gone one step further by eschewing wood for bamboo. Bamboo is a species of grass. A bicycle made of grass.

If you're thinking this must be a kind of beater that you'd just throw in the shed for a rainy day, think again. Most of the custom versions cost several thousand dollars. So they're not just a novelty, unlike the fold-up "paratrooper" bike I had when I was a kid that probably dated back to World War II—these are the real thing.

Craig makes an eloquent case for the bamboo bicycle: "My dog was playing with a bamboo stick and I thought, well, it's going to break real easily because her teeth are making deep gouges into it.... It didn't break, and I was surprised, so I thought, I should build a bike out of this stuff." This was a radical thought for a guy who pioneered the carbon-fibre frame for road bikes, but, as Craig points out, once you get past the knee-jerk reaction that something that grows up to 60 centimetres a day (and pandas eat) can't possibly be suitable for taking to the roads, bamboo is ideal.

▼ Craig Calfee dumps his bike to display its ruggedness.

According to Craig, "The beauty of bamboo is that we can choose from an infinite variety of wall thicknesses and tube diameters; for each tube we can specify exactly what we want for that particular rider. The bigger the rider, the bigger the tube, and the stiffer and stronger it is." But no matter how thick the bamboo tube is, it's still better at absorbing road vibrations, and providing a smoother ride, than other materials. How strong is the bike? Craig took on a little personal risk to show us how a bamboo bike can take a road spill and keep on ticking.

The straight pieces of bamboo tube have been joined to make the bike frame. Each joint is glued with super-high-grade epoxy glue and wrapped with hemp fibre for stability—another sustainable feature. "This material is amazingly strong," according to Craig, "yet it's light and tough. It's similar to fibreglass, but it grows out of the ground."

So Calfee's bamboo bikes have a definite high-end, responsible-consumer appeal. They're expensive but built from sustainable materials. However, Craig Calfee hasn't stopped there. Realizing that bamboo is grown all over the world, he's begun bike-building operations in Africa.

One of the bike workshops is in Ghana. Craig explains, "The idea there is to give them something that they can become more self-sufficient with. The bamboo is plentiful in Africa, and they need a lot of bikes, but a lot of people can't afford to buy a bike that's imported from China, for example. So we've

▲ Frames of bamboo tubes held together by glue and hemp.

taught a group of people there how to build their own bikes out of bamboo." Not thousand-dollar road bikes, but efficient, long-lasting transport. In fact, this international initiative has grown dramatically since we talked to Craig: it's now up and running in several countries, and you can import a bike from these fledgling industries. Check out www.bamboosero.com.

There's an irony to all this: the invention of the first bicycles back in the early 1800s was triggered partly by the need for a new mode of transportation caused by horses' death from starvation in the UK, as a result of the "Year without a Summer." That prolonged cold snap was in turn caused by the eruption of Mt. Tambora, halfway around the world in the Indian Ocean. A climate crisis created the bicycle.

Craig Calfee's bamboo bikes have the smallest carbon footprint of any modern bicycle. A tiny step toward preventing another climate crisis?

THE SUPERCAR

REMEMBER THE FIRST CARS, AT THE beginning of the twentieth century? Well, no you don't, but most of them were slow, they weren't very powerful (sometimes they needed to back up steep hills), and they even had real wood trim, not the cheesy plastic version. Those were the days. Chances are, the only time your car has come into contact with wood was when you backed into a tree.

But while the automotive world has turned its back on wood, one man, in North Carolina, thinks that rejection was unjustified and premature. He's building a car that not only has wood trim, but is *mostly* made of wood. And it's not just a car—it's a supercar, with a projected top speed of 320 kilometres per hour, run on a 600-horsepower motor!

Joe Harmon is his name, and his vehicle is called the Splinter. The car is actually a grad school project, so it may not be up and running

▶ It's not just gorgeous; it's not just tremendously powerful; it's made of wood!

▲ Even the spokes are made of wood.

for a while, but it's a designer's dream. When we caught up with Joe and his team, they were putting the finishing touches on the body—the wooden body. If you think a wooden car is something like a log with wheels, a Flintstonesque throwback, you'd be so, so wrong. Harmon is treating wood the way you'd treat carbon composite materials, shaping, bending, even *weaving* it. And while it's pretty obvious that you can't make engine parts out of wood, it's amazing what you *can* make.

Take the suspension. As Joe himself says, there was much sarcasm when he and his team first started talking about using wood for the suspension, but in the end, they realized that when it comes to what it does, the typical spring on a car isn't unlike a longbow: it bends, absorbs the force, and returns to its original shape. Then it was only a matter of finding the right wood, and that's osage orange, the strongest wood in North America. It has actually been used for bows too, and although it wasn't that easy to find (they had to get it from Kentucky), they're confident those wooden springs will do the job.

Heat is also an issue: wood doesn't really like as much heat as a twin-supercharged V8 engine generates, like 1000 degrees Celsius.

▲ The body panels are made of *woven* wood.

◄ One of the major challenges: keeping the wood away from the heat.

So they decided to run the exhaust out of the top of the engine by reversing the flow of the cylinder heads. Then they put the muffler outside as well and had it do double duty as the wing over the back of the car. Joe warns, though, against leaning on the wing after the car has been running: "Your arm might stick to it."

When we caught up with Joe and the team, they'd already been working on the Splinter for more than seven hundred days. As Joe said, "We're trying to show that wood isn't an antiquated, low-technology material. Our core woods are maple, hickory, and birch, typically, just for their strength and availability."

Cherry and walnut are used for decorative parts, like the spokes in the wheels. Those wheels are something: it took 270 kilograms of pressure before the all-wood spokes broke. And it's all wood between the hub and the tire.

In this car, wood asserts itself as a miracle material. As Joe says, "Wood can be used almost as an organic carbon fibre—if you do it right." For instance, the first of four body panels is *woven* wood. "We had to weave this wood because trying to get wood to conform to a compound curved surface is like trying to wrap a piece of paper around a globe." Some of that weaving is actually done by hand.

Nobody, not even Joe Harmon, thinks cars of the future are going to be made of wood. But who cares? The Splinter is a beauty, not just as a supercar, but as an idea.

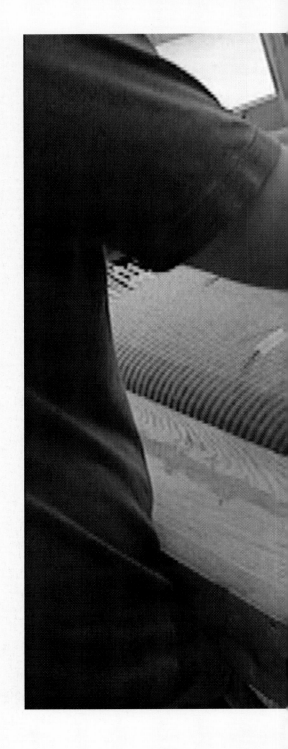

▶ Woven wood forms the foundation of the Splinter's body panels.

COSTA RICA

The man beside me is the late Alexander Skutch, then ninety-five, one of the great birders of all time. He had lived in Costa Rica since the early 1940s, when his house was completely surrounded by rainforest—but by the time *Daily Planet* visited in 1999 a veneer of jungle around the house was encircled by farms growing coffee and sugar cane. The good news is that progress is being made toward establishing a biological corridor from his place to the nearest intact rainforest.

LIFE *IS* A BEACH

SCIENCE IS AT ITS BEST WHEN IT CALLS your attention to a wonderful attribute of something you've completely taken for granted. In this case, that something is sand, and its fascinating qualities are many. Sand is so much more than the stuff of beaches and sandboxes: shake it or wet it and you get peculiar physics, inspect it with a microscope and you see unearthly creatures, and in some places in the world, if you walk on it you have to watch out for giant, wind-blown structures that seem to have a mind of their own. We've experienced all of these on *Daily Planet*.

Footprints in the Sand

Even the most commonplace experiences on a beach have their secrets. Next time you're at the beach, walk on the smooth, dark band of sand that lies between the water and the lighter, dry sand of the beach. With every step, the sand beneath your foot blanches momentarily, then darkens again. Physicist John Swain (a man who lives, breathes, and shares physics) met me on the beach one day to explain. When it comes to the chameleon footprint, John told me, it's not so

◀ The Animari are just one of the many fascinating types of creatures *Daily Planet* encountered on the beach.

93

▲ Sometimes exploring physics is as simple as taking a step on the beach.

squeeze the spaces out, when you step on sand, the individual grains can slide away from each other sideways and that opens up spaces below your foot and the water flows in, leaving a dry layer of sand on top. Of course, when you take your foot away, the water rushes back in. But it's true: once sand is reasonably well packed, as is the case on a beach, the stuff actually does sort of expand on being squeezed.

So why is wet sand dark, and dry sand light? It's the water again. Water between the grains acts as a light guide, channelling more sunlight down into the sand than it reflects, and so the sand looks dark. When the sand is dry there's no such effect, and the light is free to bounce around, reflecting off the shiny surfaces of the sand grains and back to your eye. So it appears bright and white.

And, as John pointed out, the intact parts of the sandcastle I had built were wet; the parts that had crumbled were dry. Somehow wetness created a force that held the sand grains together, and John was sure he knew what it was: "That force is the amazing force of surface tension. Water likes to attract water; water sticks to water. It's the water sticking to itself that is the glue holding this castle, or at least the wet parts, together. Water surrounding the sand grains attracts the water around other grains, and the whole thing holds together."

much the sand underfoot as the water in it that creates the impression:

The white sand is actually dry sand; the brown sand is wet. And that's exactly what you're doing when you put your foot down: you're drying the sand out. Sand is an amazing substance. It packs together in a wonderfully sort of loose way, full of little holes and spaces. And while you might normally think that when you step on something you'll

The Beach as Rainforest

Mix a little water with sand and you get an excited physicist. But add a microscope and the biologists are hooked too, or at least a few of them are. Because sand, whether it's on a beach or in a stream, is home to myriad tiny organisms, many of which have never even been given a name.

A few years ago *Daily Planet* visited the laboratory of one of the scientists intrigued by this micro-zoo. It wasn't really a complicated lab setup—just a microscope and some sample bottles set up in his home. At the time, Dr. Robert Higgins was a research professor of biology at the University of North Carolina at Asheville, and he'd devoted his career to the study of what are called *meiofauna, meio* meaning "lesser," a reference not to their importance, but to the size of mesh screen you need to sift them out.

Though they may be small, their numbers are anything but: a handful of beach sand might contain ten thousand individuals of dozens of different species. And the variety of what's there is stunning: there are spiny worms, smooth worms, shrimplike creatures, tardigrades (the

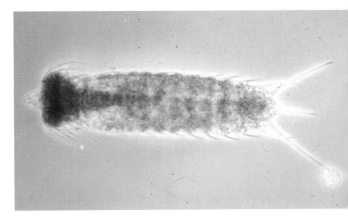

▲ *Centroderes spinosus.*

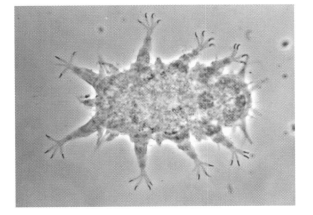

▲ A tardigrade, or "water bear."

▲ A little crustacean called *Derocheilocaris typical.*

so-called water bears that use the claws on their eight legs to grip the sand grains as they move), rotifers whose whirling circle of cilia wash food into their mouths, and creatures that can shape-shift to squeeze through tiny spaces between grains. Most have claws or suckers (or both) to cling to the sand. Dr. Higgins discovered vast groups of them himself, but there are many yet to be described. He says: "Probably many of the samples that are in the collections of the National Museum of Natural History in Washington are for posterity. I probably won't in my lifetime get through all of them. In all, there are probably millions of species that have no name."

Yet for all their anonymity, meiofauna have one striking quality. They are scavengers, cleaning up dead and rotting material, and without them, the world's beaches would be, in Dr. Higgins's view, stinking mudflats. But beyond their importance down there at the bottom of the food chain, Dr. Higgins also sees their charm: "It's another world—it's a special world. It's a world that I can identify with, because these are all my little friends down under the microscope."

Sand in the Lab

University of Toronto physicist Stephen Morris and I have shared many hours together checking out subtle bits of physics. One memorable investigation dealt with a property of sand that seems almost otherworldly. Stephen began with a beaker containing a mixture of table salt and black sand. The grains of sand were about a third the size of the salt crystals. Stephen made the odd claim that in situations like this, with a mixture of grains of two different sizes, it's extremely difficult to mix the two uniformly. In fact, your attempts to do so are likely to *unmix* them:

"You might think that this mixture is like a fluid and that if you shake it up it

▶ Stephen Morris, the "unmixer," explains sand's more mysterious properties.

◄ "The longer the tube turns, the more unmixed the two kinds of grains become."

should mix up like a fluid, but in fact granular stuff, or sand, doesn't flow like a fluid at all. For instance, if I tilt the beaker, only the surface flows, and inside that surface flow there are all sorts of processes that favour one grain's motion over the other and give you an unmixing effect."

In case I was skeptical of fancy physics claims with no evidence to support them, Stephen set up a demo: a long glass tube shaped like a fluorescent light, mounted so that it could turn slowly, with some of the same sand and salt mixture inside. You'd expect that the slow turning would equate to stirring, and that eventually the salt and sand would be perfectly mixed. But be careful when you bet on nature! When we returned to the tube minutes after setting it in motion, the exact reverse had happened: where before there had been an almost uniform mix of white and black grains, we now saw stark, alternating bands. It was a beautiful example of unmixing. But why? The secret lies in the fact that even though the grains look smoothly mixed, close

examination would reveal tiny irregularities, minuscule peaks and valleys, running from one end of the tube to the other. As the tube turns, not only does the mixture turn with it, but the grains also move from side to side because of those irregularities.

"What's happening here is that the big grains [the salt] prefer to flow at a smaller slope angle than the smaller ones," Stephen explained. "The sand prefers higher angles. And it turns out that if you start a mixture with any tiny fluctuations in slope or concentration of black and white, it's unstable. As the tube turns, in places where there are a few more small grains, they'll build up steeper slopes; any large grains will slide down those slopes into the valley next to it. And that's where the larger grains were starting to collect anyway, so the longer the tube turns, the more unmixed the two kinds of grains become."

One group in Mexico left their tube running for a month and ended up with all the black grains at one end and all the white at the other.

The Sandfish Lizard

The number-one lesson from Stephen Morris's demonstration is that while sand might seem like a liquid, it doesn't really behave like one. How then to explain the sandfish lizard, a small lizard native to the deserts of North Africa, which can—in less than a second—burrow into the sand, and then *swim through it*? That was intriguing enough for Dan Goldman at Georgia Tech to check it out. Dr. Goldman's interested in how things move, with an eye to creating robots that can go places where humans can't, and swimming through sand certainly qualifies as something we can't do!

So he brought some sandfish lizards into the lab, provided them with glass beads as a stand-in for sand, and watched. He knew that the lizard's

▼ This lizard is equally at home above or below the sand.

▶ Dan Goldman's group puts the sandfish lizard through its paces in a tank of glass beads.

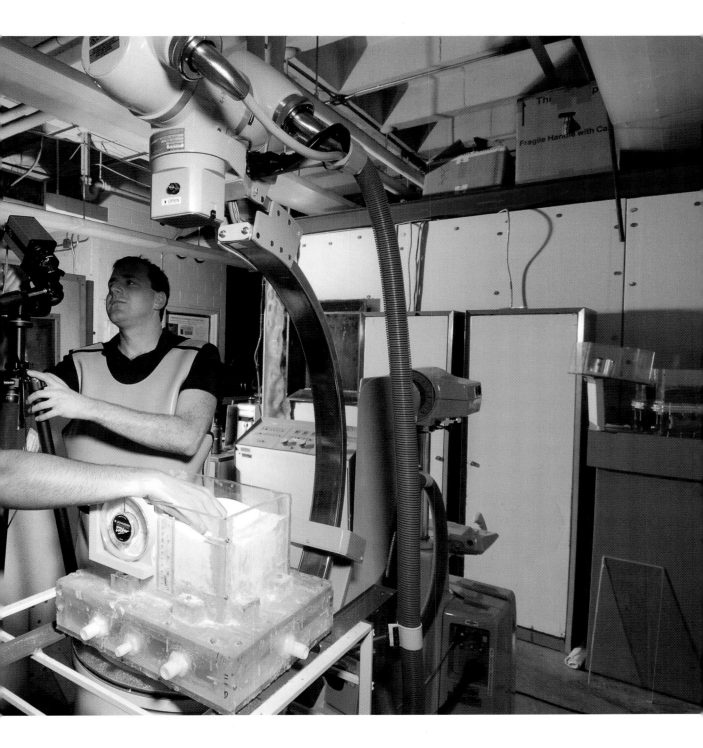

smooth scales and pointed muzzle must be adaptations for moving through the sand, but Dr. Goldman said he wasn't sure exactly how they worked:

"Initially we wanted to understand what the animal did, so we filmed it with high-speed video, and once within the medium we then we realized that the visible-light high-speed cameras were insufficient to give us some insight into what was going on. So we obtained high-speed X-ray imaging equipment."

The X-ray images were a revelation. Dr. Goldman and his team saw that the animal *wriggled* its way through the sand: "The animal was no longer using its limbs to move within the sand, but was instead propelling itself forward using large-amplitude undulations of its body, a wave travelling from its snout to its tail." Unlike animals of the same size that swim through water, like eels, whose waves tend to get bigger toward the tail end of the body, the sand lizard's movements were consistent along the entire length of its body. The pattern resembles that used by tiny aquatic worms when they swim. Even when Dr. Goldman and his research team packed the glass beads tighter by blowing air through them, the sandfish just upped the frequency of its waves and was able to move just as fast. "The rough rule is that the animal does the same thing regardless of the compaction of the material," Dr. Goldman explained. "And that was the big surprise."

There's still much more to learn: for instance, computer models can calculate how the frictional force between the lizard and sand grains would change if those body waves were bigger or more frequent. In the end, according to Dr. Goldman, the lab wants to export that information to the manufacture of what they call "subsurface locomotor devices"—robots that can do the same thing: "We'd like to hope that some of the principles we've discovered about how the animal moves can inspire the next generation of devices that can actually move in complicated shifting material."

As to exactly what such robots might be capable of, the only limits might be those of the imagination.

▶ Analyzing the forces on every segment of the sand lizard's body reveals that its snake-like movements are perfect for overcoming drag.

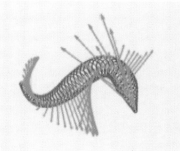

Animari

And finally in this *Daily Planet* tribute to sand, a little technology, a little biological illusion, and an artistic triumph: Theo Jansen's Animari—beach animals.

"The Animari are walking animals," Jansen explained when we visited him in Holland, "and they have the advantage that they don't have to eat. They get their energy from the wind." These skeletal creatures are made from PVC tubing and elastics, and Jansen assembles the versatile tubes so that they're not just structural, but can be assembled into pistons as well. When air passes through the tubes, the pistons move, and that in turn allows these giant assemblages, the structures he calls "wind walkers," to move.

▼ Not only fascinating to look at, they move and behave like living things.

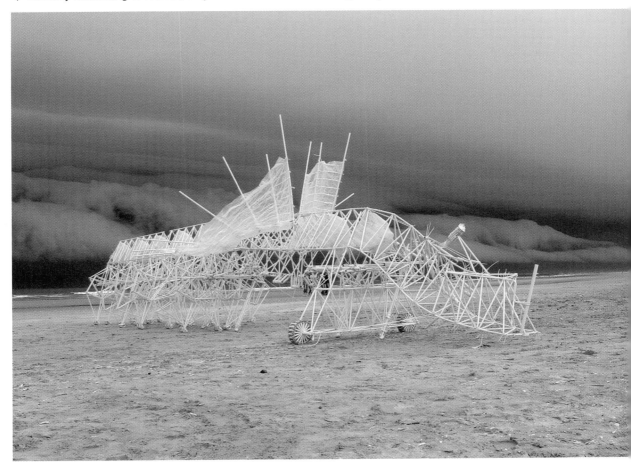

But that simple description doesn't do them justice. While it's remarkable enough to have created huge, spindly structures that shuffle up and down the beach (high-stepping so the feet don't get bogged down in the sand), Jansen has built in some additional features, all of which are designed to allow the Animari to live on their own one day. For instance, they're equipped, oddly enough, with lemonade bottles: "When there's enough wind, the wings come out, and while moving, they pump air into the bottles, and this is the spare energy that they can use when there's no wind anymore."

Lemonade bottles as batteries? That's not the end of Jansen's ingenuity. Using the same simple materials, he has created a counter that helps the structure establish exactly where it is on the beach between the dunes behind it and the surf in front. If indeed it does venture too close to the water—which would quickly incapacitate it—a dangling tube senses the water and reverses the direction of the Animari. There's even a mallet that can anchor the creature into the sand to immobilize it in the event of a storm. And make no mistake: Jansen's goal is to allow these constantly evolving life forms to inhabit Holland's beaches independent of human help:

"When these animals walk on the beach, and they can do that independently, then I've put something on the earth just like a child, and the one thing that a child can do is be independent one day. So I hope these animals will walk there on the beach forever when I'm gone."

▲ Theo Jansen created his extraordinary Animari from very ordinary materials.

IT'S CLOTH ...
BUT IT'S
CONCRETE

WILL CRAWFORD AND PETE BREWIN have had one of those ideas that makes you ask "Why hasn't someone thought of that before?," just as Thomas Henry Huxley couldn't believe how simple his friend Darwin's theory of evolution was. But it's important to think of something, no matter how simple it appears, before anyone else does. Will and Pete have created something called "concrete cloth"—it combines the rigidity of concrete with the flexibility of cloth. They wouldn't tell us exactly how it's made—they're protecting their intellectual property—but it's a thick piece of cloth, open-faced, with dry cement mix held in place by the fibres of the cloth and a PVC backing to provide waterproofing. It's a thick cloth, but not so thick you can't fold it or bend it or put it into any shape you like.

That flexible piece of cloth can be transformed into a hard concrete shell just by adding water. So imagine draping the cloth over a frame, then playing a hose over the cloth until it's soaked

▼ This unusual material combines concrete's rigidity with cloth's flexibility.

▼ Easily assembled, concrete cloth shelters can serve a variety of purposes, such as emergency medical centres.

▲ Out of the sack and complete—ready to use—within 24 hours.

through. You have about four hours to fuss around with the shape before it starts to seriously harden. Twenty-four hours later, the cloth has turned to solid concrete, and you've created a hard-shelled, waterproof, flameproof structure.

One such structure is the concrete canvas shelter. Will and Pete's inspiration for this was the common egg: the shell is thin, but it's also very resistant to being compressed or crushed. So they got the idea of creating an inflatable plastic inner lining over which the concrete cloth can be laid and glued. Both are folded and sealed into a plastic sack, and the sack is transported to wherever it's needed. Once in place, the shelter is unfolded, inflated, pegged to the ground, and sprayed (with either fresh or salt water), and you've got a building! And here are the numbers: a 25-square-metre building assembled in forty minutes by two people, ready in twenty-four hours.

The buildings stand on their own, but they may not need to. Snow, sand, or earth

▲ Snow, rather than being an inconvenience, is simply insulation.

▲ A chair with very, very firm cushions.

can be packed against the outer walls as reinforcement, protection, and insulation. But the most amazing feature of this material is the number of uses to which it can be put: emergency housing in disaster areas, military buildings, ecolodges, covers for dikes in flooded areas, roofing, erosion control, ditch linings, and pipeline covers. That's surely only the beginning. I swear I even saw a concrete chair.

Yeah, it's a simple idea. Too bad none of us thought of it.

▲ Like concrete cloth, Dynamic Air Shelters represent exciting new possibilities for temporary building needs.

DYNAMIC AIR SHELTERS

IN A GRIPPING PIECE OF VIDEOTAPE, A violent explosion creates a shock wave that spreads out from the epicentre of the blast, like the ripples from a stone in the water. As the shock wave spreads, it flows around and over a temporary shelter, its walls flapping, the entire structure rocking and rolling. But moments later it's over: the structure is intact and unaffected. Then you find out it's made of cloth and air—nothing more.

This shelter was constructed by Dynamic Air Shelters, a company with a foot in both Newfoundland and Alberta. Its temporary buildings can be delivered to a site folded up, and be pumped up and ready to go in less than two hours. Their strength in the face of shock waves and blasts is obvious from the way they move when struck—it's not about rigidity and strength, but rolling with the punch, allowing the energy to flow around and through the structure, rather than *at* it.

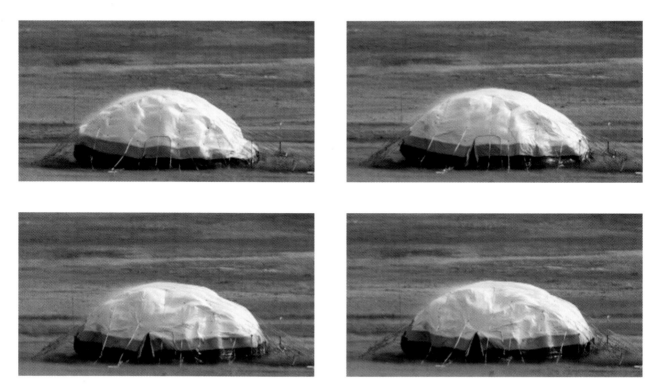

▲ As the shock wave from the explosion rolls over the shelter, it bobs, weaves, and recovers with ease.

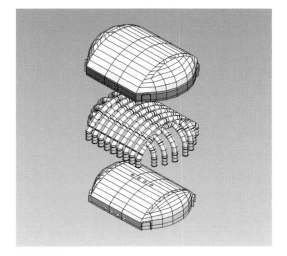

▲ The three layers and how they're bound to each other are the secret to the shelter's stability.

Each shelter is built from three layers of fabric, draped over and attached to columns, also made of cloth, that reach right up from the ground to the peak, with hooplike "hug straps" attached at regular intervals. The material is a tough PVC-coated polyester vinyl, huge sheets of which are welded together. The resistance of the columns if you punch them doesn't betray the fact that they're merely filled with air. Tim Guss emphasizes the structure's flexibility: "It's got the firmness of a car tire, but it's actually only one pound per square inch that holds this structure and the air columns up. You can push this in about 10 inches with a forklift before it'll actually rupture."

But the secret to these shelters' ability to withstand powerful blasts apparently lies in those hug straps—in their ability to move, slow down, stop, and recover. The straps are tied to elasticized connection points, which allow the air columns to move initially before being pulled back. It's the architectural version of passive resistance—each column is independent and holds everything up, but if you didn't have tension pulling the columns they'd fall apart as soon as the shock wave passed.

Tim explains, "The shelter absorbs some of the load but also redirects the energy; the shelter flows through that and then rebounds to its original shape."

The shelters are versatile too, able to resist industrial explosions, car bombs, and even much more concentrated forces, like artillery debris. The advantage is their portability and speed of deployment, so even crime scene investigations can be housed in them.

In the end one of the best parts of this story has nothing to do with advanced technology or clever engineering, but with people's lives. Dynamic Air Shelters are manufactured in Grand Bank and Fortune, Newfoundland, two towns hit hard by the fisheries' decline. The shelters themselves are designed to save lives, but the jobs they create are, in a sense, lifesavers too.

▲ Inside the shelter: a vast space, flexible but strong.

METEOR CRATER, ARIZONA

This crater is immense—1.5 kilometres across—but its size doesn't do justice to the upheaval that must have accompanied its creation fifty thousand years ago. The object that dug out the crater was probably only about 50 metres across, but it was travelling an estimated several kilometres a second when it struck. A hundred years ago the crater was thought to be the result of a volcanic eruption. But in the early 1960s conclusive evidence emerged that it was in fact created by an enormous impact—making it the first proven example of an extraterrestrial object striking the earth.

FOUR

How Animals Work

Sometimes the best way to learn how an animal works is, strangely enough, to make an artificial version. It can also help to put that animal in a situation it's never been in before, like walking on a treadmill. But sometimes, as you see here, the best way to learn about an animal is to actually look *inside* it.

ROBOTIC
ANIMALS

IN FIFTEEN YEARS OF PROGRAMMING, *Daily Planet* has revealed an unbelievable number of robots. Many of them, like Honda's famous Asimo and the Korean Albert Hubo, are very human-like. Others bear no resemblance to us at all and are designed either to augment human effort, like the University of Calgary's NeuroArm, which performs neurosurgery, or even to replace humans completely, like the barbot, the mechanical servant who brings you a drink when you get home from work.

Of course, Mars rovers are robots too, and we've seen plenty of them, although many haven't yet reached the surface of the red planet and, indeed, might never get there. The wild variety, the designs that don't get past the drawing board, are testaments to the fact that robots haven't left the experimental phase: scientists and engineers are still trying to figure out how best to use them.

▶ Albert Hubo and Bullwinkle: robots with very different purposes.

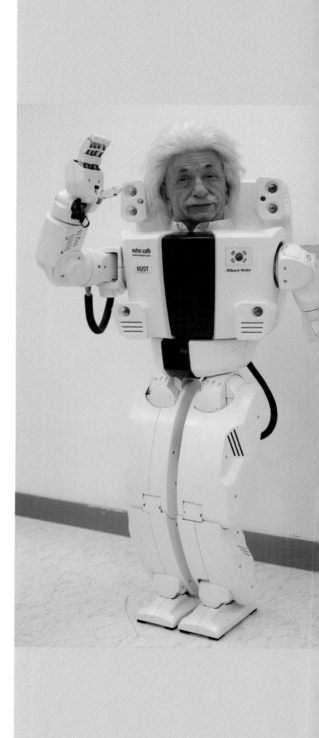

▲ This male sage grouse wants to know: "Am I showing off enough to win her heart?"

When you line them all up, to me the most intriguing robots we've seen on *Daily Planet* are the robotic animals. But wait a minute—aren't robots supposed to improve on nature, not imitate it? Well, it depends on what you want them to do.

Take this little beauty. If you were a male sage grouse, you'd be so smitten by this female of the species that you wouldn't even notice that she has a mechanical under-carriage and is running on rails. In fact, you'd be too busy showing off all those features that make you an outstanding male

▲ Sadly, the robot female sage grouse doesn't have a heart to win.

▲ Gail Patricelli putting the finishing touches on Fembot.

and fabulous mate candidate: the spiky tail feathers; the amazing yellow air sacs framed by white feathers on your breast (at first glance like two sunny-side-up eggs bobbing up and down); and the distinctive pops, whistles, and gurgles you produce while you're strutting your stuff.

That's strutting, literally: male and female sage grouses meet in the spring on an open patch of prairie called a *lek*. The females are there to choose a mate from among all the males, and each male is doing his best to convince the ladies that he's the one who should be chosen. But how is it that some males are very successful in finding mates, and others not, when to the human eye there isn't much difference among them?

That's where evolutionary biologist Gail Patricelli comes in—along with her bionic female companion, Fembot. Dr. Patricelli wanted to know what makes successful sage grouse males tick, but to find out she needed to control some of the action on the lek. She can't control real females, but she has total authority over Fembot. So rather than trying to follow free-ranging males and females, Gail uses Fembot to track the behaviour of individual males and, she hopes, reveal some of their secrets.

She can turn her head from side to side for that "I'm-a-real-sage-grouse-female-on-the-prowl" look.

Here's how it works: early in the morning, before the birds are active on the lek, Gail and her colleagues put Fembot on her track (a G-gauge electric train track—that's 4.5 centimetres wide, or a little less than 2 inches). The scientists retreat to a blind and run Fembot out onto the lek by remote control. She looks real because she once was: her skin and feathers were taken from deceased females. She can turn her head from side to side for that "I'm-a-real-sage-grouse-female-on-the-prowl" look, and best of all, she can orient her entire body toward a male that the scientists want to watch. She's equipped with a microphone that emits female sounds, and a video camera to record her suitors' behaviour. If everything runs according to plan, sage grouse males will indeed approach and display in front of her. That should be as far as it goes, because Fembot never delivers the final "I'm yours!" signal. (Although that didn't stop one male from mounting the robot anyway. I wonder if mounting the robot is something like jumping the shark.)

She may not have been riding the rails for long, but Fembot has already delivered the scientific goods. Gail Patricelli has seen that the most successful males (the ones that she knows from previous observations have mated with real females most often) are capable of the most vigorous displays, but they don't perform wildly and indiscriminately. Instead, they pace themselves, waiting for Fembot to get into range before inflating their air sacs and uttering their pops and whistles. By contrast, less successful males seem to be not as capable of fine-tuning the timing of their displays and end up hitting what for them is full stride as soon as they're on the lek, no matter where the females are. As a result, their performances—already somewhat diminished compared to those of the best males—are wasted.

Gail Patricelli doesn't do just sage grouse. Her first robotic companion was a female satin bowerbird, and although this bird lives on the other side of the world from the sage grouse, in eastern Australia, the robot revealed a similar twist in male behaviour: the best males know how to dial up or dial down their courtship.

The male satin bowerbird builds his bower, a short archway, out of curved twigs and branches, and scatters brightly coloured objects in front of it. The male of this particular species prefers blue things, like pieces of glass, feathers, ballpoint pens—virtually anything it can find. If a female is at least tentatively interested, she'll enter the bower and watch as he prances around back and forth, flapping his wings, jumping over the bower, hissing, buzzing, and chattering, picking up objects and offering them to her, getting more and more excited and demonstrative. But it's a fine line the males must walk, because although females like intense displays, they can be frightened if they're *too* intense. If that happens, the female becomes unsettled and eventually flees, and the whole thing is called off.

In the case of the sage grouse, successful males don't waste their time displaying if females aren't within range. Satin bowerbird males that know when to ease off the intensity are also more likely to be victorious. But how do they know when to do that?

That's where Gail Patricelli's robotic female bowerbird, nicknamed "Jaime Sommers" (the Bionic Woman), came in. Patricelli engineered her to be able to crouch, a move she'd seen real females do in the midst of intense male displays. Patricelli suspected that crouching was a signal of encouragement to the male, a sign that the female could tolerate his vigorous

▲ The demure Jaime Sommers waiting for a male to impress her. Or at least, waiting for a male to *believe* he has impressed her.

performance. But having a robotic bird made it much easier to control the timing and degree of crouching and get clean, interpretable data. Sure enough, Jaime Sommers and Gail Patricelli together showed that the really successful satin bowerbird males monitored the robot's crouching and tailored the intensity of their display as a result.

One thing Gail Patricelli's work clearly shows is that amorous males, whether they're bowerbirds or sage grouse, tend to overlook tiny details like model railroad tracks and metal legs when they're intent on finding a mate. How far can you push this deception? Jose Halloy, at the Free University of Belgium, will tell you: pretty far. He created robotic cockroaches that look nothing like the real thing. They're closer to tiny model cars than anything else, but he has fixed them up so that a colony of roaches accepts them as fellow insects. How? Smell. Many insects depend on airborne chemicals called *pheromones* to guide their behaviour. Ants are a classic example—they use pheromones to lay down trails for other ants, to tell who is friend or foe, and even to sound the alarm. Roaches are no different, and once Halloy wrapped his model roaches in filter paper dabbed with roach pheromone, the real insects lost their fear of the robots.

That in itself is an interesting discovery, but Halloy wasn't finished. He'd programmed his roach robots to move randomly about an enclosure and sense what was going on around them, but also to gather under two kinds of shelters: very dark or much lighter. Real roaches prefer the dark shelters three-quarters of the time, but when Halloy introduced as few as four robots to a group of twelve roaches, and the robots gravitated toward the brighter shelter, the real insects, influenced by some sort of mysterious social pressure, followed them there. This finding has given some hope that future Pied Piper robots could lure thousands of cockroaches to their deaths, despite any instinctive misgivings they might have. Whether a brain roughly the size of the point of a ballpoint pen (with one neuron for every hundred thousand we have) is capable of misgivings is another question.

▲ These robots smell ... well, just right. The real roaches accept them without question, even following their lead.

"If You Go Out to the Woods Today, You're Sure of a Big Surprise"

NOW THIS IS ONE MAGNIFICENT ANIMAL, AN ICONIC CANADIAN CREATURE: the moose. There might be a million of them in the country. They're common in Newfoundland, New Brunswick, and the forests of the western provinces, but much rarer in other parts, like Nova Scotia. And they're huge: the biggest moose ever recorded, a male, weighed 1800 pounds and stood almost 8 feet tall at the shoulder. Male moose are commonly over 1000 pounds, with females averaging something like 700 pounds. If you were to happen across this particular animal on a walk through the woods, you'd certainly be startled …

▲ This magnificent moose appears completely at home in its wooded surroundings …

… But not for the reasons you might think. That's right, this magnificent animal is a robot: robomoose, otherwise known as Bullwinkle. Unlike other robotic animals that have appeared in these pages, robomoose sheds light not on the behaviour of its own species, but on that of humans—specifically, poachers. The Nova Scotia Department of Natural Resources uses robomoose to tempt such hunters into firing killing shots in its direction. Unfortunately for the hunter, Natural Resources officials are lurking in the woods nearby and pounce on him mere moments after he pulls the trigger. Moose poaching may sound like the kind of "good idea" that would occur to the Trailer Park Boys, but

it's serious business in a province where the species is endangered.

It didn't take long after robomoose was deployed to catch the first victim. And no wonder: the robot is amazingly lifelike. Officers with the enforcement division of Natural Resources place the moose in the woods just off the highway, then hide a short distance away. They have a remote-control device that can turn the moose's head from side to side as he calmly stands there, waiting. If the temptation is just too much, the would-be hunter aims and fires, and to his (short-lived) delight, the moose falls on the spot. What he doesn't know is that the officers have remotely pulled out the pins that hold the moose upright. But

▲ … but, as many poachers have discovered, it's just as much an interloper as they are!

he finds out soon enough when they arrive on the spot and arrest him.

Robomoose—Bullwinkle—has many cool features: the motor to control his movements is placed near his tail so that it avoids damage from even the most inaccurate of hunters; he weighs just a little more than 25 kilos, fits easily into the back of a pickup truck, and requires only a few minutes to set up. And, best of all, robomoose appears to be working. Even though he sustained several (nonfatal) bullet wounds early on in his career, lately he has escaped unscathed. When I was writing this, John Mombourquette, director of the enforcement division of Nova Scotia's Department of Natural Resources, contacted me with these comments:

Since its appearance on Discovery Channel, we've used the robotic moose on many investigations. We are pleased to report that it hasn't been shot since your show aired. Poachers are reluctant to shoot a moose, as they aren't sure if it's real or one of ours. Many have seen our moose—some raised the gun, others tried to scare it, and some took pictures/video—but no one has been brave enough to shoot. Your coverage of our moose was beneficial in getting the message out that we're using this type of technology. Thank you.

We appreciate John's thoughts, but let's face it: the success belongs to Bullwinkle.

▲ Deiter Warwick, Mike Hunter, John Mombourquette, and Bullwinkle. Bullwinkle's the one in the back.

IRENE PEPPERBERG,

PROFESSOR OF PSYCHOLOGY AND ANIMAL COGNITION SPECIALIST

I'm sure Dr. Irene Pepperberg would forgive me if instead of including a quote from one of her *Daily Planet* interviews, I quoted instead the subject of those interviews, the African Grey parrot Alex, with whom she worked for decades. Alex demonstrated to the world that he could, if not *master* language, use it in a masterful way. His ability to utter English words revealed a depth of comprehension equivalent to that of young children. When shown a tray of different-coloured objects and asked which ones were green, he could say "Keys." Moreover, when the question was changed to "What colour cube?," he could correctly respond "Blue."

And when Alex tired of all this testing, he said what most of us might say in the same circumstances: "Wanna go back [to my cage]." Alex died in September 2007 at the age of thirty-one.

ANIMALS ON TREADMILLS

THE BAD THING ABOUT TREADMILLS IS THAT THEY DON'T actually go anywhere. (This made their circular cousin, the treadwheel, perfect for use in Victorian prisons as a vehicle for exercise-as-punishment. And in modern times if you feel as though you're on the treadmill of life, you're really in trouble.) The good thing about treadmills? They don't go anywhere, making them useful for urbanites (and hamsters) who can't stay in shape any other way, and, perhaps surprisingly, for scientists. Without treadmills, researchers couldn't begin to understand the subtleties of animal movement.

Think of the most captivating images you've seen on Discovery Channel: wildebeest stampeding, killer whales erupting out of the water, T. Rex charging at the camera … all dramatic images that attract our attention instantly, probably because we evolved brains that are attuned to rapid movements by large, threatening animals. Scientists, of course, are always interested in something beyond the instant reaction, in the "why" and "how," and you can't answer those questions adequately by watching animals in their natural habitat. You need to bring them into the lab and put them on … a treadmill. That's odd enough, but when you see the variety of animals that have been put through their (stationary) paces, it's positively mind-blowing. Here are some we've featured on *Daily Planet* over the years, in no particular order.

Alligators

Dr. Colleen Farmer at the University of Utah has been working with alligators for more than a decade, and a few years ago she and her fellow scientists trained them to walk on a treadmill. Small alligators, that is, only about a foot long—Dr. Farmer made it absolutely clear she wouldn't try this with full-size gators. They weren't an overnight sensation, either; it took three months or more of very gentle, persuasive handling before the animals built up their endurance and could negotiate the treadmill for as long as three or four minutes. But Dr. Farmer wasn't so interested in how they walked as in how they breathed while walking.

There's a curious fact about lizards (to which alligators are related): they can't breathe and walk or run at the same time. A view from above tells the story: with each step a lizard takes its body bends, and so it undulates back and forth as it moves, almost like a fish. That movement compresses first one side of the body, then the other, but to breathe an animal has to be able to expand both sides of the body at the same time. So lizards alternate: run, stop, breathe, run, stop, breathe.

But alligators present a bit of a puzzle because some features of their bodies, like their posture and their circulatory system, suggest that they should be capable of speed and endurance, even though they rarely

◀ It takes alligators a long time to acclimatize to a treadmill …

▶ … but in the end they yield fascinating science.

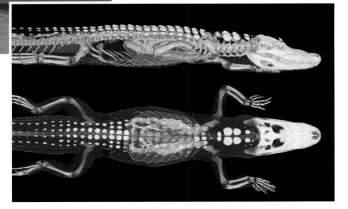

display that, preferring to live their lives as sit-and-wait predators. So the question was, What goes on in their gator bodies when they're forced to walk for a few minutes?

Something very cool, with implications far beyond alligators. When Dr. Farmer's group compared their recordings of air flow in and out of the animal with recordings of muscle activity from various places in the body, they found that a *pelvic bone* actually helped the gator breathe continuously as it was walking. The bone, which in most other animals is anchored securely and can't move at all, can be pulled back and forth, toward and away from the animal's tail as it walks, altering the space in the abdominal cavity, and making breathing easier.

But why would alligators have this fancy mechanism for breathing while moving if they appear to do not much more than lie around waiting for dinner to walk into reach? Maybe it's a reflection of their past—their very distant past. Some dinosaur species, like duck-billed dinosaurs, stegosaurus, and triceratops, had pelvic bones suspiciously similar to these unhinged pelvic bones in alligators. Colleen Farmer wonders if this means that even before the dinosaurs, the animals ancestral to the trio of alligators, dinosaurs, and birds evolved this breathing aid. If that's true, it might mean that the gators of long ago were much more mobile, and therefore fiercer, than they are today.

Shrimp

Shrimp on the barbie, maybe, but shrimp on a treadmill?

> We were just amazed. We weren't sure what a shrimp would do on a treadmill; we knew that shrimp are very active animals and they can migrate long distances, but we were surprised at how well they performed. They could stay active for hours at a time, way longer than we wanted to run our experiments … they didn't even slow down when we weighed them down with miniature backpacks. We ran out of film, we had to go for lunch, so eventually we just had to stop them rather than trying to exhaust them.

▼ A treadmill just right for a shrimp.

▲ Shrimp like this outlasted their human observers, so dedicated to the treadmill they were.

Wow! Their project is to exhaust shrimps? There's an intelligent rationale behind this, and the man who explained it all to us is Dr. David Scholnick, a biologist at Pacific University in Forest Grove, Oregon. He and colleagues at the Grice Marine Lab in Charleston, South Carolina, were interested in the effects of disease on marine organisms, with shrimp as the model, and they set out to compare the performance of sick and well shrimp on the treadmill (fashioned from a tire inner tube). Unfortunately, these days there's no problem finding sick shrimp. David's colleagues in South Carolina see them all the time in fishermen's catch. There may be multiple causes, but the effects, once the ailing shrimp are on the treadmill, are apparent: they just don't perform well.

Dr. Scholnick explains, "We think the decrease in endurance and speed has to do with the fact that they're having trouble getting oxygen across their gills; part of the immune response is that their gills are getting clogged up and they're having trouble breathing. This may make them more vulnerable in low-oxygen environments, which are becoming much more common in coastal areas, and possibly make them more prone to predation."

▶ The question is, "How does walking upside down change the way the sloth's legs work?"

Next on the menu? Blue crab. Since we interviewed Dr. Scholnick, his collaborators at the Grice Marine Lab have run these crabs and found that even when their metabolic rate drops by 30 to 40 percent once they're infected with bacteria, they still manage to maintain their normal level of aerobic activity on the treadmill. The scientists expect that while the crabs are resilient in ideal lab conditions, that won't be the case in subpar waters.

Sloths

Okay, now you're sure I'm kidding, right? Putting a sloth on a treadmill could only have a bad ending. But if the treadmill were a tread*pole* instead, then that's different. Sloths are the only mammals that motor around upside down, clinging on to branches with their curved claws, so a treadpole is the only way to keep them in one place to study them.

And of course now you're thinking, Sloths are the slowest animals in the forest already—they move only about a quarter of a kilometre an hour even when they're in a panic—so why go to all the extra trouble to set up a treadpole to slow the animal down a little more? Good question.

We followed the sloth to its lair in the University of Jena lab of Martin Fischer and John Nyakatura. The treadpole was there; so was the X-ray imager that would take a thousand images per second of a moving sloth. Once the animal started to pull itself along the treadpole, amazing high-resolution X-ray video of its skeleton filled the computer screens. The sloth's movement was smooth and sinuous, nothing like you'd expect. Suddenly it makes good sense to study how sloths move.

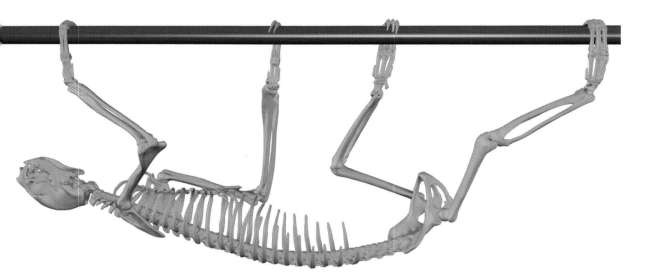

▲ So obviously a four-legged animal with a pretty standard skeleton, but so different at the same time.

"They *are* the only mammals that walk upside down," Fischer explains. "One of the interests is how gravity impacts on locomotion. So normally when you see a horse or a dog running, gravity is a friend of these running animals, because they really use gravity during locomotion. But if you're upside down like the sloths, what does gravity mean to you? We have no idea, and that's why we're studying these animals."

Early results from analysis of the X-ray images show that the sloth's forelimb—or arm—movements are similar to those used by animals who are right side up. When they want to speed up, they just extend their arms farther, spend less time hanging on, and go faster—it's pretty straightforward. Their hindlimb movements have changed much more to adapt to treetop life, but overall there's nothing shocking about the way the sloth has evolved.

What's really curious is that the two species of sloth, two-toed and three-toed, are only distantly related. The two-toed go back to some of the ground-dwelling giant sloths that died out about ten thousand years ago; the three-toed don't have any obvious relatives at all. The two species split off from each other an estimated 30 million years ago, long, long before there were any even vaguely recognizable human-like creatures on earth. But, once separate, the two species independently came up with similar solutions to the problems posed by spending your life hanging upside down from a branch. Maybe one day X-ray video will show subtle differences in their locomotion that betray their separate origins.

Wallabies and Wombats

Once you've seen shrimp and sloths on treadmills, wallabies and wombats don't seem the least bit unusual. They're quite different from each other, wallabies bouncing like springs, wombats shuffling their way along close to the ground. But getting a good idea of what exactly is going on inside these animals as they move was the late Russell Baudinette's goal. As he told us, "We don't know very much about how much energy animals expend when they move; movement is hard to measure. You've got to bring them into the lab; you've got to train them to hop on treadmills, or to run on treadmills."

▲ The wallaby accelerates as the treadmill revs up, but, amazingly, it uses no more energy to do so.

> "They're the most beautifully engineered animals around. They can hop, they can carry loads, and they have this beautiful respiration system that leaves us for dead."
> RUSSELL BAUDINETTE

When Baudinette did that with wallabies, he got a shock. Wallabies are built like kangaroos (although smaller), and they can use their powerful hind legs to move easily on a fast-moving treadmill. And then something strange happens: "If we run a dog on a treadmill, its rate of oxygen consumption increases. But with these animals, once they start to hop, the oxygen consumption will stay the same; they'll hop along and not use any more energy. They're the only animals we know of that can do this."

It sounds suspiciously as if they're getting something for nothing, but those are the data. As the treadmill accelerates, the wallabies speed up too, but somehow they seem to be able to do it effortlessly. Even when a female is carrying a joey, adding 20 percent to her weight, her energy consumption stays steady. Baudinette added weights to his wallabies to simulate that burden—no effect on them either.

To maintain a given speed, a wallaby uses less than a third of the energy used by a four-legged animal of the same weight. Dr. Baudinette suspects this might be an adaptation allowing the animals to range far and wide across the Australian landscape, and he thinks that three spring-like tendons in the hind legs enable this endurance, by recovering up to 90 percent of the energy they generate, storing energy every time the feet hit the ground and bounce back. Most sports shoes can manage only 60 percent. As Baudinette said to us, and I don't think anyone would disagree, "They're the most beautifully engineered animals around. They can hop, they can carry loads, and they have this beautiful respiration system that leaves us for dead."

The wombat is a different story. These marsupials have been called "fat," "slow," and "stupid." I don't know about that, but chunky, short-faced, short-legged, and short-tailed they are, and they're sometimes unwilling to play the treadmill game. Occasionally they just stop and are carried helplessly backwards; sometimes they make it worse by turning and heading in the wrong direction. Even when the wombat pulls it together and heads along the treadmill, it seems to be doing so with incredible reluctance.

The wombat digs elaborate burrows with numerous chambers and spends much of its time underground. And some of that lifestyle seems to have rubbed off on its metabolism, because it burns energy at only about two-thirds the rate of an equivalent marsupial living at the surface. If its oxygen supply is lowered it will breathe faster, but the response is slow and relatively weak, as if this is a situation that crops up occasionally underground, explaining why the wombat is prepared for it and needs only a minimal response.

There are other animals walking on treadmills out there somewhere, and in time, we'll have them on the show too.

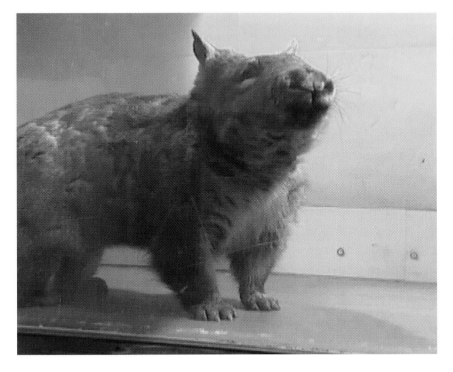

◀ Wombat on a treadmill—a reluctant participant.

A TRIP TO WOLONG

THE *DAILY PLANET* TRIP TO THE WOLONG Panda Reserve in Sichuan Province, China, was a wonder. A beautiful, relatively uncrowded part of the country, the Wolong area is prime panda habitat: mountainous, with the sides of those mountains covered in bamboo. When we were there, in 2006, only about 1600 pandas were still living in the wild, and 100 or so made their home at the reserve. Wolong itself was amazing to see, but we were extraordinarily lucky that two hugely important events happened during our two days there.

The first was a world-record mating (yes, they do keep such records, especially when the animal being observed is so rare). For years pandas had been very reluctant to reproduce in captivity; it was thought that the males were too weak, lazy, ignorant, or a combination of all three. Efforts to improve the chances of the pandas mating by, for instance, making males more physically

▶ Baby pandas: just as charming as this photo suggests.

140

fit by forcing them to climb for their food instead of simply handing it to them, were apparently beginning to bear fruit, literally. The number of newborn pandas was rising steadily. But mating was still a crapshoot: females are fertile only two or at most three days a year, and putting a fertile female together with a male didn't guarantee anything happening.

The day we were at Wolong, a male with a great mating reputation, Ling Ling, was put together with a young, inexperienced female, Ximei. The outlook wasn't promising: Ximei had refused a different male the day before. One thing became obvious right away: pandas don't insist on privacy. They displayed all the usual panda mating moves and vocalizations, even though every keeper in the place seemed to be watching, cheering them on, making rude jokes, and—this is the key part—holding stopwatches.

Once Ling Ling had said or done the right things, panda style, the two animals were locked in an embrace. Even then there was anxiety all round, because sometimes panda sex lasts for only a few seconds, and the longer it goes on, the better the chances of a pregnancy occurring. They shouldn't have worried: twenty-nine minutes and ten seconds later, the bears finally parted, having set a world record for panda mating, breaking the old mark by several minutes.

▼ Xiang Xiang, just a day before his ill-fated release into the wild.

Cellphones were brought out to spread the good news, and if there had been champagne around, it surely would have been uncorked. Even better, months later Ximei gave birth to twins.

Establishing a viable captive-breeding program at Wolong is only the first step: the ultimate goal is to repopulate the wild panda habitat. There's no point in bringing new panda cubs into the world simply to export them to various zoos. When *Daily Planet* was at Wolong we were lucky to visit the first panda to be released into the wild after being born and raised in captivity. His name was Xiang Xiang, and his official release was to happen a day or two after our meeting.

We climbed a steep mountainside to see him in his pre-release enclosure, a huge area about the size of a wild panda's territory, designed to acclimatize him to his future life in the wild. This was a great privilege for us, because his exposure to humans was being strictly limited prior to his release. Liu Bin, Xiang Xiang's keeper for most of his five years, located him via the panda's radio collar. But pointedly, neither Mr. Liu nor any of us joined Xiang Xiang inside the enclosure: he treated it as his own and likely would have attacked.

Xiang Xiang was chosen to be the first captive-bred panda to be released because at age two he was judged to be the strongest and healthiest of all the males at Wolong. From that time on he'd been prepared for release, and now he was in his final days

▲ A baby panda demonstrates its specialized wrist bone—and its devastating powers of cuteness.

of captivity. It was a little like visiting the first human to go to Mars just before launch. The hopes of the panda program at Wolong, and to some degree all of China, were resting on Xiang Xiang.

Sadly, the experiment failed. About six months after release, Xiang Xiang was found dead. Apparently the cause of death was a fall from a tree, but there was evidence that he'd been wounded while fighting off other pandas. Wolong experts surmised this might have been a territorial battle and vowed to choose a female for their next born-in-captivity release.

Xiang Xiang's short and apparently violent life in the wild contrasted dramatically with the scene in the Wolong nursery, the enclosure reserved for pandas less than a year old. There were seventeen of them when we visited, and they could have passed for big, playful, fun-loving puppies. We had a limited amount of time in their enclosure, and I wanted to use that time to describe their "thumb," which isn't really a thumb at all but a specialized wrist bone that they use to hold and manipulate bamboo as they eat it. What better opportunity than to have a panda cub in my arms, a cub so cooperative that I could hold its front paw and actually show the wrist-bone thumb?

I did have to tell the story twice because one of the three panda cubs that were all over me kept pawing and biting my microphone. But in the end, I managed to tell it from beginning to end. And we aired it. As a piece of science journalism it was a total failure. I'm sure absolutely no one listened to a single word I said, because they were so riveted by the antics of the three cubs. Somebody should have told me that panda cubs are über-cute. I could have just stood there and smiled. Sometimes you have to know when to shut up.

▲ Richard Wassersug throwing himself into his science.

▲ A panda apparently inspired by Richard.

P Is for Posture

For years Richard Wassersug of Dalhousie was our "Weird and Wonderful Science" columnist. One memorable Richard story about pandas featured the males' different styles of peeing. One thing you should know about Richard: he's a gamer. At times he was willing to do things on camera that even I wouldn't do. I swear I once saw him dip a sandwich into a beaver pond at my cottage, then take a bite. So I wasn't quite sure what to expect.

However, his story was, as usual, edifying. Richard pointed out that in the panda version of dog versus fire hydrant, it's not just which tree you use, but how high up the trunk you can pee. Males actually stand on their hands while peeing. And it works—all pandas show more interest in the highest marks, but subadult males are wary, because those markings suggest the presence of a giant animal.

Handstands aren't the only panda peeing posture. There's also squatting (facing the tree), reverse (back to the tree), or leg-cock (like a city dog). It's mostly females and subadults that squat, more males leg-cock than females, and only adult males handstand; all these styles fit together to make up a set of dominance signals. Or lack thereof.

Back to Richard. My fear that he might recklessly act out this story was groundless. He did illustrate the squatting, reverse, and leg-cock positions, but he drew the line at doing a handstand in the studio. And he was, as usual, entertaining.

CHINA

Of course we had to take pictures on the Great Wall, but really, like the Taj Mahal in India, as impressive as this national icon is, it misleads by its narrow focus. Travelling to China to cover science and technology took us to other places, like the record-breaking Sutong bridge as it was being constructed over the Yangtze River (where a skimpy thigh-high bamboo barrier was all that kept anyone from tumbling into the water below) to a factory in Wuhan, Sichuan Province, where brass bells identical to those discovered in an ancient tomb are still forged today. An F1 racetrack, a giant shipyard (for making giant ships of course), and the restoration of the emperor's summer palace all caught our eye, and all became part of *Daily Planet Goes to China*.

CYBERLIZARD

AS TECHNOLOGY ADVANCES, ANIMATED characters in movies, both humans and animals, have become much more realistic. But in a lab in Australia, researchers have turned the technology around: they're animating creatures not for our entertainment, but to understand nature better.

Chris Evans runs the lab at Macquarie University in Sydney. His goal is to figure out what animals are trying to communicate to others when they engage in displays. The animal of choice is the Jacky dragon, a small lizard native to Australia. These animals are territorial and competitive, and when faced with a new lizard in their territory they perform a complicated set of movements, including push-ups and arm waving, all of them sending some sort of message. And if those fail to intimidate their rival, they leap into attack mode.

▶ "Are you talkin' to me?" The territorial Jacky dragon establishes its boundaries.

▲ A life of either aggression—or submission.

dramatic or more subtle. Cyberlizard is the virtual version of Fembot (see page 121). And don't assume it was drudgery to create cyberlizard: these scientists refer to the computer technology and the graphic effects with such affection that you just know they loved doing it.

But the science of the lizard's behaviour is the most important thing. If I told you that arm waving, push-ups, body rocking, and tail flicking all seem to be important messages, what would you guess they're saying? You might speculate that push-ups are a "Hey man, I can do push-ups forever" kind of statement. A sign of dominance. You wouldn't be far off, especially when you compare push-ups to arm waving.

There are two kinds of arm waving, slow and fast. The fast ones are aggressive, as you might expect, and the slow are gestures of submission. Sometimes the conversation is pretty straightforward. For instance, if one lizard is doing extremely fast push-ups, the other, in acknowledgment of that demonstration of strength, performs the submissive slow waves.

But this is complicated stuff. For instance, Dr. Evans and his colleagues expected that if cyberlizard acted submissively, real lizards would cut back on their own aggression, figuring that they had won the duel. But that's not what happened: submission actually increased aggressive responses. They wondered if that might be because the real animals were confused by the fact that cyberlizard was sending

Obviously the lizards know exactly what all these movements and their combinations mean, but for us, it's not so clear. What is he trying to say with all those push-ups? Why are they so fast? What persuaded the other lizard to back down?

The problem is, with two live animals signalling like crazy, it's just too chaotic to sort out the key messages. So Evans and his colleagues decided to simplify things a little by creating a virtual Jacky dragon, a *cyberlizard*. Combining top-level animation technology with a stuffed lizard, they created an extremely realistic version of the animal that moves its tail, limbs, and body just like the real thing.

The beauty of cyberlizard is that his movements are completely controlled. They can be sped up, slowed down, made more

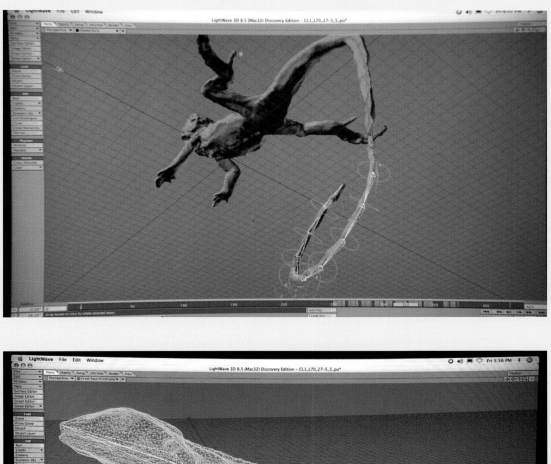

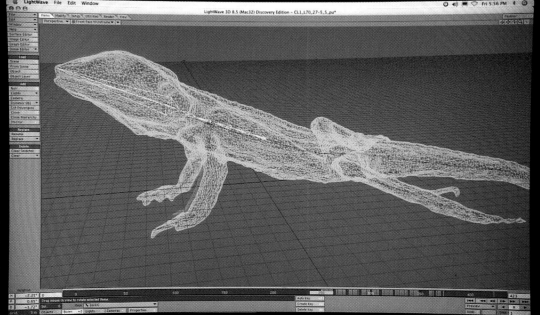

▲ Top-level animation technology—and a stuffed lizard—were used to create a realistic-looking cyberlizard.

submissive, slow arm waves, but was not retreating, as most Jacky lizards would. That inconsistency might just prompt the real lizard to continue being aggressive, probing the defences of this unusual lizard.

You can imagine just how many things you could do with cyberlizard. For instance, what is the threshold between a slow arm wave and a fast one? Is there some grey area here that's ambiguous to other lizards? What happens when cyberlizard behaves weirdly, at least by lizard standards? The reptiles' displays are a painless way of defusing competitive situations. If they resorted

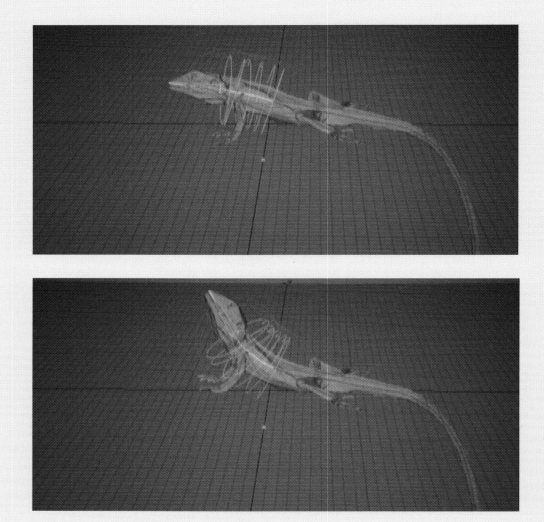

▲ Cyberlizard, in its final form, is good enough ...

to actual attacks each time there was a challenge, many would be fatally injured.

And why stop with lizards? There's an Australian snake called the death adder that waves the end of its tail to attract Jacky lizards. Apparently they mistake it for insect prey. So the lab guys created a cybersnake, and showed that the two speeds at which it waves its tail correspond to the speeds with which the Jacky's most common prey—beetles, ants, roaches, and so on—move. Oh yeah, that also involved creating *cybercricket* to test the Jacky's reactions. It's hard to know what's real anymore.

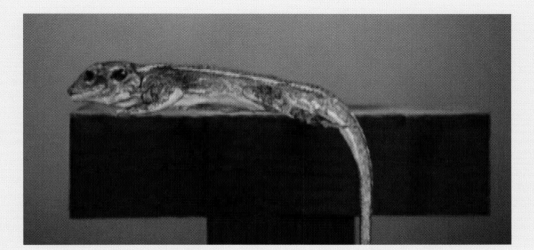

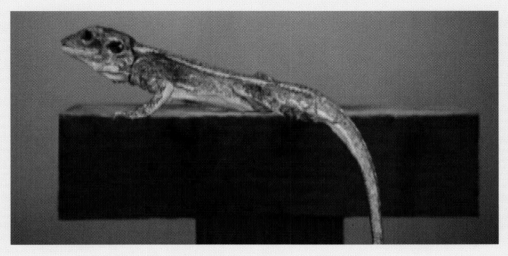

▲ ... to convince the real thing that he has a rival.

FRASS AND
FECULA

PICTURE LIFE AS A CATERPILLAR ... WELL, okay, it's not that easy to imagine you have a long, baggy body on multiple legs and spend your time chewing on leaves. What's worse, you'd have no clue that one day you'd be transformed into a spectacular, winged beauty of a butterfly.

It's fortunate that caterpillars have extremely limited brain power because it *is* a dull life. For many species, caterpillar days are spent inside a rolled-up leaf. Why a rolled-up leaf? To make it harder for predators or parasites to find you. But spending days inside the same leaf creates its own problems. For one thing, what about all the frass (or fecula) produced during that time? Those are technical terms for feces, or poo.

Caterpillars are generally not very efficient digesters, so a lot of frass could accumulate in that confined space. Depending on how tightly the leaf is rolled, this might lead to very crowded conditions. It's also possible that disease-causing bacteria or fungi in the frass could threaten the caterpillar's health if they were allowed to accumulate. But most important, the odour of growing piles of frass could attract those very enemies that the caterpillar seeks to avoid by living in a rolled-up leaf in the first place.

▶ Caterpillars like this have to resort to, ah, unusual techniques to avoid being discovered by predators.

A

▲ The 76-yard field goal, caterpillar style.

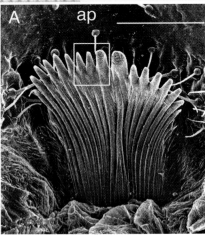

A   ap

▶ The scanning electron microscope reveals the exquisite design of the anal comb, a key component in the process of "frass" ejection.

Faced with this dilemma, some caterpillars have adopted a radical strategy—they launch their frass, firing it as far as they can. For some species that's a considerable distance: the caterpillar of the skipper butterfly can launch packets of frass close to forty times their body length, or more than 150 centimetres by a 4-centimetre-long animal. That has been compared to a human kicking a 76-yard field goal, a record in any league.

To achieve such impressive distances, the frass has to blast off with an initial velocity of as much as 1.5 metres per second,

and one of the most pressing scientific questions has been, How can a soft-bodied caterpillar do that? The answer, as usual in the natural world, is to employ a uniquely elegant mechanism.

This all happens, reasonably enough, at the caterpillar's back end. It's kind of complicated back there, but one of the essential pieces of equipment is something called an *anal comb,* a multi-pronged piece that sticks out from the caterpillar's rear. When a piece of frass is ready for ejection, it arrives at the rear and triggers a series of subtle adjustments. The last set of legs (which aren't real legs at all, but just little protrusions from the body) detach from the surface of the leaf, allowing the abdomen to lift into the air—think of this as raising the barrel of an artillery gun from the horizontal position. Then the anus opens, and muscular contractions start to push the frass pellet through that opening. All this time the anal comb is acting as a latch, preventing anything dramatic from happening.

But that doesn't last long. As the tissues around the frass retract, revealing more and more of it, blood pressure starts to build up in the terminal segment of the caterpillar's body—called the *anal plate*—that the frass is resting against. The pressure builds … and builds … and builds … T minus 3, 2, 1 … blast off! The comb, which was acting to restrain the plate, now slips off; the plate is released, driven against the frass by its own blood pressure, and strikes the frass like a bat hitting a fastball; the caterpillar can now return to eating more leaf (and making more frass), confident that it has left no trace of itself for its enemies to detect.

Given the relative violence of the whole procedure, it's probably lucky for us that no creatures bigger than these caterpillars have evolved to launch their feces. But I'm surprised that no enterprising group has inaugurated a frass-launching competition—after all, the scientists who analyzed the launching mechanism were easily able to persuade caterpillars to perform the feat in front of video cameras. I'm sure the presence of a cheering crowd wouldn't inhibit them either.

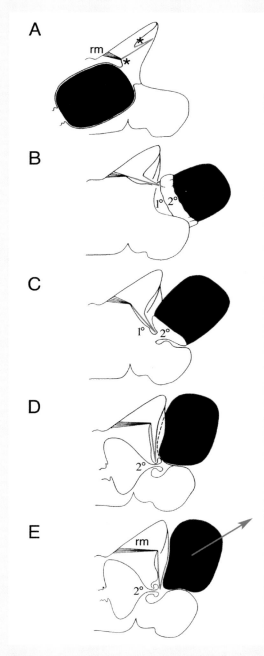

▲ The frass (in black) is gradually moved into position by subtle adjustments of the surrounding structures, then, in a flash, launched.

TOM EISNER,
ENTOMOLOGIST
AND PROFESSOR
OF CHEMICAL
ECOLOGY

"When I was a boy and was beginning to get interested in insects, I used to do something that most entomologists don't do: I used to pick up the insects and smell them. And I was quick to notice that many of them had a real stink. So I got curious about that. I wasn't very old—I think I was about nine or ten. I would taste them, and I found that they tasted worse than they smelled. That's how I came up with the idea that insects must be chemically protected, and now that I'm a grown-up entomologist, I know that that's the case. Insects are among the most protected animals on earth. They have the most incredible chemical weaponry, and if I were to take you for a walk in the woods and just pick up insects randomly, you'd see what I mean."

GROUNDED
GOLLUM

WE'VE DONE COUNTLESS STORIES ON *Daily Planet* about close relationships between humans and animals: Jane Goodall and her chimps, Irene Pepperberg and her African grey parrot Alex, and the myriad people who've gone so far as to build prosthetics for animals and birds that have suffered injuries. There's a bond between us and other living things, something that the evolutionary biologist E.O. Wilson called *biophilia.* For my money, the strongest expression of biophilia we ever saw was between Steve Eales and a vulture.

Steve and his wife ran Hawk on the Wild Side, a falconry centre in England. Although Steve kept a crazy variety of animals there, everything from goldfish to ferrets, it was really about the birds of prey. Steve wanted visitors to Hawk on the Wild Side to get an appreciation of just how magnificent these birds are—up close. But even Steve, who obviously has a big dose of biophilia, had his favourites:

▶ Steve Eales and Gollum.

"I just love big birds, and I love vultures in particular because they get such bad press. It's a bit of a quest to try to educate and let people realize what wonderful characters they are … they're not these hideous, horrible things that just rip things to pieces."

Among those vultures, one of the most special to Steve was Gollum, an African white-backed vulture. Gollum is a striking bird, but when we met them both, he had one singular deficiency. He couldn't—or wouldn't—fly. Apparently he hadn't flown for some time, and all Steve knew was that the previous owner had never even encouraged Gollum to take wing.

▶ Gollum has all the flying equipment all right, but even with Steve demonstrating proper technique, he chose to stay firmly anchored to the ground.

162

As Steve pointed out, "We pride ourselves on flying birds well, which is why it's been a bit of an embarrassment that he can't actually do it. But I'm going to work and do everything I can to make sure that he does end up flying."

Now there's a claim that should bring you up short—Steve is going to work to make Gollum fly? How on earth could he do that?

His first attempts were well meaning but not very successful: Steve simply ran across the field with Gollum in pursuit, hoping that flapping his arms would inspire the vulture. That, and the food treats Steve had in his pocket. The food was a mixed blessing: it did prompt Gollum to follow Steve, but as Steve pointed out, why fly when the food stays on the ground?

Steve concluded, "The low-tech field method has great limitations because there's nothing to make the bird actually take off." Gollum did spread his wings and at least skip along the ground though, just enough to persuade Steve to maintain hope.

But the next step involved a piece of good luck. In nearby Milton Keynes, a unique business opened its doors. Airkix is a vertical wind tunnel that provides indoor skydiving; it allows people who don't actually want to jump out of an airplane to experience the thrill of freefall, suspended by giant fans generating supporting winds of 225 kilometres per hour. Steve was entranced: could this be a better way of getting Gollum airborne? Airkix agreed to give it a shot; they

▲ A vertical wind tunnel helped Gollum to spread his wings!

reduced the wind speed to a more vulture-friendly 32 kilometres per hour, and Steve stood in with Gollum perched on his wrist. Progress! Gollum, although tethered to Steve, spread his wings much farther and for longer than on the ground, and seemed to be learning how to hang on the breeze, looking at times as if he might actually have it in him. As Steve pointed out, having that fan-generated updraft was much more like riding thermals off the edge of a cliff, as vultures do, than running along the ground.

When we left the two of them, Gollum was flying—yes, actually flying—tens of metres toward Steve. Steve was ecstatic, not for himself, but for the bird: "I'd love for him to be able to come into a big arena and actually do a big circuit of the arena so everybody's looking up at him from underneath rather than looking down on him and laughing at him because he isn't flying."

Now *that* is biophilia.

STONE-HANDLING MONKEYS

I LOVED JAPAN. THE FOOD IS GREAT, even on the bullet train. Life is pretty intense too—for every garden there's a Shibuya Square. The first science thing I did on my trip was go to the Arashiyama primate reserve on the outskirts of Kyoto. Here, a colony of Japanese macaques live in the forest but come down the mountain for food, to be "provisioned." There they hang out, behaving, as far as anyone can tell, more or less normally: fighting, having sex, trying to have sex—the whole gamut. That's where I first saw *stone handling*: monkeys sitting by themselves and playing with a handful of stones—picking them up, putting them down, shifting them around from one hand to the other, clacking them together. One of the macaques might get up suddenly and leave the stones behind, only to find another handful and start playing with them.

Stone handling is amusing to watch, but scientists have been fascinated by it. It seems to have no purpose—it's a huge stretch to imagine that it could have any survival value—and appears simply to be something the macaques do *when they have the time to do it*.

Stone handling has been seen only in troops that are regularly provisioned. For a wild animal, being able to count on food being provided, same time, same place, is an incredible luxury. So what do they do with this unaccustomed bounty? They play with stones. How human!

To be fair, some inventive monkeys have turned stone handling into stone throwing, and in so doing might have given the habit some use after all. They throw the stones underhanded, and it looks as if they're using it as part of a display. Now if it's part of a display, and that determines who mates with whom, then it's more than just play, it does have a use, and the toy has become a tool.

It's pretty clear that provisioning is a key factor in stone-handling behaviour. Some monkeys do it more, and with greater intensity, when there's food around. If the food is withheld, stone handling dies away. Provisioning might even have triggered the invention of stone handling in the first place, although that doesn't begin to explain how and why it was invented, or by whom.

There has to be a "whom," the first monkey to do it. In 1953, in a colony on the southern Japanese island of Koshima, a female named Imo began washing the sweet potato that scientists provided before eating it. By 1962, about three-quarters of the monkeys over two years old washed their sweet potatoes. Imo was a genius, a Marie Curie of macaques, because she also came up with the idea of spreading mixtures of wheat and sand on water to allow them to separate—the sand would sink, leaving the wheat behind to be eaten.

I was excited to see stone handling when I did, before every monkey starts throwing the stones around and making them useful. I liked the habit just as it was: idle play.

▲ Now let's see: I'm well-fed and have really nothing much to do—I think I'll play with stones!

PEOPLE WE'VE MET

RICHARD LEAKEY,

PALEO-ANTHROPOLOGIST, CONSERVATIONIST, AND POLITICIAN

"I think increasingly wildlife in Kenya and other African countries is going to be confined to land that's specifically maintained for the purposes of wildlife. I think it's unrealistic to expect people to reduce their standards of living because wild animals are roaming. When I moved to this home where we're doing this interview there were wildebeest, zebra, and buffalo roaming on this land. Now all around where we're sitting there are homesteads with fences, they're growing corn, raising cattle, and the lion has gone, the hyena and leopard have gone. The buffalo have gone. There is nothing here.

"Just down the valley here I have a vineyard, very small, just 5 acres, but it's got some good grapes in it. And I can tell you, one troop of baboons that breaks through the electric fence can destroy 5 tons of grapes in one afternoon. Now, I do it as a hobby … I can buy wine. But if your entire livelihood depends on what you're doing on your land, and an animal that is allegedly owned by the state comes in and destroys it, it can't be very encouraging."

WALKING
IN CIRCLES

WE ARE VISUAL CREATURES, AND THIS was never more strongly demonstrated than in *Daily Planet*'s story about walking in circles. There have always been stories of people getting lost in the woods or the Arctic and ending up circling endlessly without realizing it, but Marc Ernst and Jan Souman of the Max Planck Institute in Tübingen, Germany, felt the stories lacked hard data, and they set out to provide it.

The stunning thing was the variety of ways they tested the tendency to walk in circles: they had volunteers walk in the woods, slog across the desert, trudge across a field blindfolded, and, finally, walk on the incredible CyberWalk, the only omni-directional treadmill of its size in the world.

▶ If you think you can walk a straight line blindfolded, think again.

▲ Marc Ernst and his roaming volunteers test the built-in human biological compass.

As Marc explained, "There's a lot going on in your body that allows you to orient yourself: you have your eyes, ears, the vestibular system in your inner ear that helps you balance yourself, and your legs that move you through space. The question that we're addressing is, How do all these cues work together and help you orient yourself?"

The tests of people walking in the forest and the desert established that we actually can keep roughly to a straight line, especially if the sun is shining. There are distractions, particularly obstacles that force you to change your course temporarily, but in general we're pretty good in those circumstances. What's really interesting is that over the course of a couple of hours or more the sun changes its position significantly, yet somehow—unconsciously—we're able to compensate for that.

Then the CyberWalk. It's a treadmill all right, but a square rather than rectangular one. This shape allows it to move in any direction, so if a blindfolded volunteer starts walking straight ahead but then gradually starts turning one way or the other, the treadmill compensates. First the researchers tested walkers wearing a virtual-reality headset that showed them a forest scene that they appeared to be walking through.

He sees a virtual forest, Marc notes, and his task is to walk as straight through this forest as possible. But of course he has to avoid trees every once in a while so he can't walk perfectly straight. So the question is, does he manage to keep kind of the same course, or will he start to walk in circles?

The answer is, he pretty much stays to the straight line. But that's because he's seeing the forest around him. When blindfolded, things get a little stranger and certainly

much more interesting. The beauty of the CyberWalk is that you could actually end up walking in exactly the opposite direction and would never know it. And indeed, that's what happened in our story.

But the most convincing evidence was gathered in a field outside the lab. There, volunteers were blindfolded, earplugged, and invited to walk for four or five minutes. In a straight line, of course. Amazingly, not one but several people ended up walking

▲ The helmet allows people to get lost without actually going anywhere.

in a giant circle, arriving back within a few metres of the group standing exactly where they started. They were absolutely stunned when they found out, because they didn't *feel* as though they were circling. You couldn't have done a better job walking in a complete circle if you'd tried—actually these experiments pretty well prove that. The question is, why?

Marc Ernst is convinced that as long as you're blindfolded, the problem lies in the vestibular system in the inner ear: "It measures acceleration, both rotation-wise and also linear. In order to get a sense of direction it has to integrate all that information to a velocity and direction signal. And all those signals give you a certain sense of the direction you're walking, but they're noisy (in the sense that the information isn't clean and well focused), so every step you take, you get more and more noise in your estimate base; therefore you drift away from what is

▲ The Cyber Walk—a virtual wander through the forest.

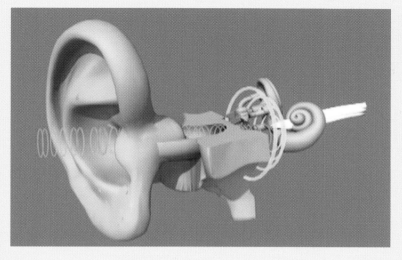

straight ahead. And in the end you're not really sure what direction you're walking."

There have been strange explanations in the past for circling when lost, for instance, like that we all have one leg stronger (or longer) than the other and it pushes us steadily toward the other side of our body—a strong right leg would make us bend to the left. It's like being right-footed or left-footed. But these experiments show that people circle in one direction one time, and the other the next—there's no consistency, so no evidence for a preferential leg. Marc and Jan tested these ideas by adding insoles to one shoe or the other to make one leg longer— both made no difference. Their experiments also eliminate the (bizarre) suggestion that people get lost when they're close to the North or South Pole because they're being influenced by the Coriolis effect, the spin of the earth that causes weather systems to form giant spirals in the atmosphere.

Even running doesn't help, although you might have thought that with speed, as in bicycling, you achieve greater stability. No matter how it's done, the outcome is the same: we walk in circles if we can't see.

But even so, plenty of details still need to be filled in, and I suspect people in Germany are going to be travelling in circles for a long time to come—under close supervision, of course.

FIVE

Canada in Space

Astronauts don't advertise this,
but they're among the most
accomplished people on earth.
Can you fly a jet fighter, speak
Russian, perform surgery, and
repair computers? Do you also happen
to be a musician and an athlete?
Okay, you qualify. And as I said—that's
on earth. Where they excel is,
of course, in outer space.

JULIE PAYETTE, on controlling the Canadarm:

"I think it's very similar to operating a construction crane on earth, except you don't have to worry about the weather! But, just like on the ground, we cannot hit something with the robotic arm, so we have to be very careful when we get close to structures. Also, we have to operate in lighting conditions that change all the time. As the shuttle and the ISS [the International Space Station] go around the earth every hour and a half, they spend about half their time, about forty minutes, in pure sunlight, then darkness, then light, then dark."

▲ ▶ Julie Payette has completed two space flights in her career, logging over 25 days in space. During the 29th mission to the International Space Station in 2009, Payette served as the flight engineer aboard the space shuttle *Endeavour*. She also operated all three robotic arms—the shuttle's Canadarm, the station's Canadarm2, and the Japanese arm on Kibo—to install scientific experiments on the ISS's Exposed Facility and deliver critical spare parts and replacement batteries to the station.

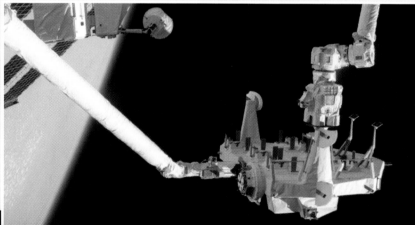

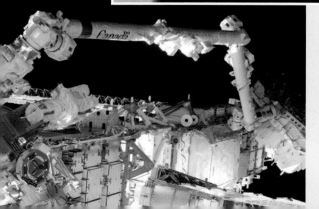

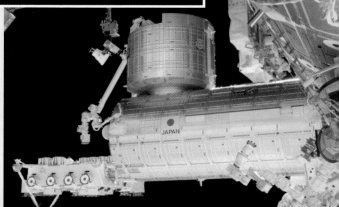

BOB THIRSK, on the difference between coming home on the shuttle and on the *Soyuz*:

"Three of us sit in a space about the size of a telephone booth, so imagine three people sitting together with five-point harnesses and pressure suits as well. Unlike the smooth descent of the shuttle, the last twenty minutes in a *Soyuz* re-entry is like a first-class ticket at Disney World. There's a lot of jolting, dynamic movement. You really feel the G effect, 4 Gs going right through your chest. On a debilitated body that's been in space for months, it's like 8 or 9 Gs. And then the landing is like a small car crash."

◄ ▼ Engineer and physician Robert Thirsk holds the current Canadian record for the longest space flight (over 187 days) and the most time spent in space (204 days). As part of a 2009 international mission, he travelled to the International Space Station on the *Soyuz* spacecraft, which launched from the Baikonur Cosmodrome in Kazakhstan. While on the ISS he performed complex robotic operations, maintenance and repair work on station systems, and life science experiments that investigated changes in plants, animals, and humans under space flight conditions.

DR. STEVE MACLEAN, on riding the Canadarm for Mission STS-115:

"On flight day four I'll be flying the arm doing that main installation task, and I'll be using the Space Vision System to guide me. Then on flight day eight I ride the arm and pick up a huge communications antenna, and holding it, the arm will fly me down and I'll install it there."

▲ ▶ Physicist Steve MacLean, currently serving as the president of the Canadian Space Agency, is the second Canadian to ever walk in space. He's been involved in two space flights and was instrumental in developing the Advanced Space Vision System (ASVS), a computer-based camera system that enhances the control of the Canadarm and Canadarm2. He was also the first Canadian to operate the robotic Canadarm2 in 2006, when the shuttle crew deployed solar panels on the International Space Station.

STEPHEN HAWKING,

PHYSICIST

AND

AUTHOR

"I think the most significant scientific observation in my time is that of the faint background of microwave radiation that fills the universe. This background has a thermal spectrum indicating that the universe was much hotter and denser in the past. This confirms that the universe began in a big bang.

"The advances that we have made since cave-person days have been driven by human curiosity and the wish to understand the universe around us, rather than the desire to make money."

CHRIS HADFIELD, on space in space:

"We really had the feel (since there were seven of us on the shuttle) that once we had docked with the station it was like coming out of a seven-guy camper van to a mansion with a swimming pool. It was just a beautiful, organized, spacious, comfortable, quiet, nicely appointed space, and when we went back to the shuttle it was cramped, smelled like seven guys, all full of gear. The space station is a much more desirable place to live in space."

▲ ▶ Colonel Chris Hadfield is the first Canadian to ever walk in space—and the first Canadian to ever operate the Canadarm in orbit. He's also the only Canadian to ever board the now-destroyed Russian space station *Mir*, during his time as mission specialist on the space shuttle *Atlantis* in 1995. He performed two separate spacewalks during the space shuttle *Endeavour*'s 2001 mission to the International Space Station, when the international team delivered and installed the Canadarm2.

DAVE WILLIAMS, on the challenge of spacewalks:

"You can be outside for six and a half hours, holding on to an object that in my case weighed 1200 pounds. People talk about zero G, but that object possesses the property of mass so it takes a lot of strength to control it. It's true: you could hold it on the tip of your finger, but when you get it moving, then you've got to be able to stop it. So imagine you're on the ice and you grab the Zamboni and get it moving—you've got to hold on to it tight to be able to stop it."

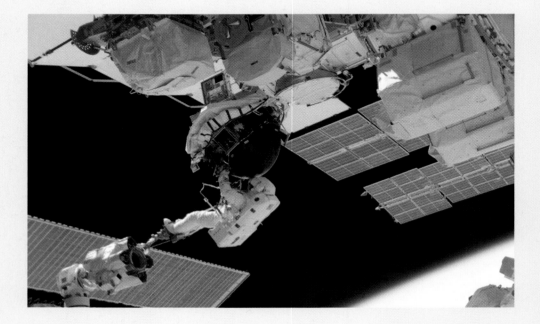

◀ ▼ Dr. Dafydd (Dave) Williams has logged the most total spacewalks performed by a Canadian astronaut (three) and the most amount of time spent on one single spacewalk (17 hours). As mission specialist on the 1998 Neurolab project aboard the space shuttle *Columbia,* he explored the effects of microgravity on the brain and nervous system. He performed his record-breaking spacewalks during the space shuttle *Endeavour*'s 2007 assembly mission to the International Space Station, adding a new gyroscope and an external stowage platform to the ISS.

BJARNI TRYGGVASON, on launch:

"Right up to a few minutes before launch it was like another training session—another simulation session. You couldn't really tell the difference. You don't really start to get a sense that, hey, this is a little different today until they start firing up the systems on the shuttle. Each time they do that the whole shuttle shudders a little in response. The impression I had was that you were sitting in this giant and it's just starting to wake up—it's coming to life."

▲ ▶ Engineer Bjarni Tryggvason was selected as one of the original six Canadian astronauts in 1983. He was project engineer for the design of the SVS target spacecraft, which was deployed during the space shuttle *Columbia*'s 1992 mission. In 1997 he flew as a payload specialist aboard the space shuttle *Discovery*, testing the Microgravity vibration Isolation Mount (MIM), which operated aboard the Russian space station *Mir*. While in space he also studied the effect vibrations have on experiments performed aboard the International Space Station.

PLACES WE'VE BEEN

MOSCOW AND STAR CITY, RUSSIA

It was a space tourist's dream: an inside look at Star City, where cosmonauts train, and later a trip to Baikonur, Kazakhstan, to see the launch of Zarya, the first module of the International Space Station. Even the bus trip into Baikonur from the airport was amazing, a veritable travelogue for the Soviet space program: we landed on the airstrip originally built for the Soviet-era shuttle called *Buran*, passed the dilapidated gantry that would have been used for the rocket to carry cosmonauts to the moon, and saw, on the side of the road, the twisted wreckage of a silo built for nuclear missiles. It had been destroyed by agreement with the United States as part of the Strategic Arms Limitation Talks. The day ended at a banquet where Russian soldiers and ex-cosmonauts tossed down enough vodka to fuel a rocket of their own.

SIX

Life or Death

The variety of life on earth
is paralleled by the variety
of death: a single chimp may
die in Gombe and the tiny local
population is seriously diminished.
A human can die and not be found
for thousands of years; others
die and are scrutinized day
by day, month by month.
From each we learn something
about ourselves.

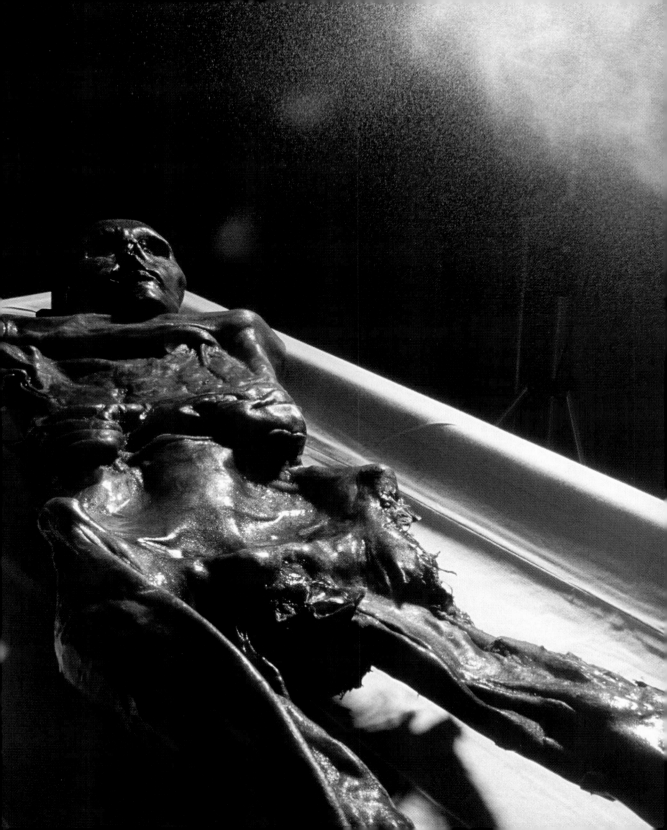

ÖTZI THE ICEMAN

ON SEPTEMBER 19, 1991, TWO GERMAN tourists hiking in the Austrian Alps stumbled upon a body partly encased in ice. Finding any body is a disturbing event; however, it soon became clear that this was a case not for CSI, but for archaeologists. The body was that of a man somewhere in his late 20s or 30s who'd lived *5200 years ago*. Because he had apparently been encased in ice shortly after his death and had remained there for thousands of years, his body had resisted decay—he was what's called a "natural" mummy. A brief territorial scuffle ensued when it was discovered that the deceased man, named Ötzi, was actually lying a few tens of metres across the border in Italy, so now he rests at the South Tyrol Museum of Archaeology in Bolzano.

◀ The ultimate "cold case": murdered more than five thousand years ago, discovered in 1991.

What a find Ötzi has proven to be: since his discovery, throngs of scientists have examined every little detail of the man, every square centimetre of his skin and even his insides. And so far, he appears stranger than any would have guessed. Some examples:

1. He was in rough shape when he died, largely due to the arrowhead that was found lodged underneath his left shoulder blade. It had severed a major artery, so even though it didn't penetrate any major organs, it likely caused him to bleed to death within minutes. But he'd also suffered a crushing injury to the back of his head, and enough cuts, bruises, and scrapes to suggest that he'd been involved in some sort of hand-to-hand combat just before he died. The arthritis in his joints and the parasites in his gut were apparently the least of his worries.

▲ ▶ Ötzi's final resting place. He was found atop the Schnalstal glacier in the Ötztal Alps.

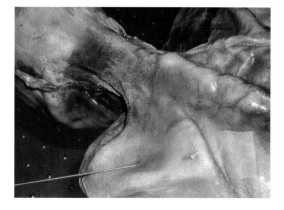

▲ This probe is inserted right into the wound in Ötzi's shoulder where the fatal arrowhead entered.

2. Analysis of the variation in the atomic composition—the isotopes—of his bones and teeth suggest that he was born kilometres east of where he was found but in adulthood had migrated to an area to the south. Tooth enamel isotopes reflect what someone eats and drinks as a child, while bones do the same for adults. In Ötzi's case, the relative amounts of various oxygen isotopes in the local water varied because rain in the north ultimately comes from the Atlantic Ocean, and rain in the south from the Mediterranean. The Atlantic is cooler, and its chemical composition reflects that. So it's actually possible to say that from the ages of three to five, Ötzi lived in one valley and migrated somewhere else as an adult.

3. It has even been possible to make some guesses about the last twenty-four to forty-eight hours of his life, partly because of pollen contamination of samples of food taken from his intestine. The remains of Ötzi's last three meals were still in his large intestine; they all contained traces of meat from two kinds of animals, red deer and ibex. But peculiarly, pollen analysis shows that over the course of those meals, he moved from high-altitude forest to down deep into the valleys and then back up to high altitude, where he died. This evidence plays into what's called the disaster theory, which, in one version, speculates that Ötzi was herding livestock in the mountains, descended to his home village, where he got into an altercation, and fled back to the high altitudes with which he was apparently familiar.

Okay, there's more imagination than science in that scenario, but it's not unreasonable, and it's a tribute to the amount of information you can get out of the kind of painstaking research that has been done with Ötzi. Besides, scenario creation is fun. Here's another:

Put together the evidence for that blow to the back of his head, the arrow wound, and the fact that his arm was unnaturally stretched across his chest, and a detailed account of his death can be constructed. For one thing, the awkward position of the arm apparently preceded rigor mortis, so it can't have been the result of anything happening long after his death, such as movement of the glacier in which he was entombed.

Here's what (might have) happened: Ötzi is being pursued and has already suffered a gash on his hand. He stops to put down his equipment and is struck by an arrow in the back. As if that weren't enough, he either falls or is pushed backward and strikes his head on a rock. But he's bleeding to death anyway. Finally, the archer rolls him over (onto his arm) and takes out the shaft of the arrow, leaving the head buried in his body. But it might be a case of "You think I look bad, you should see the other guy." Traces of blood from four other people have been found on Ötzi's gear: one sample on his knife, two different DNAs on an arrow-head, and another on his coat.

Of all the *Daily Planet* stories about Ötzi, two stand out: our description of his shoes and a re-enactment of his tattoos.

The Bata Shoe Museum in Toronto let us get up close and personal with mock-ups of Ötzi's shoes, and they turned out to be ingenious pieces of footwear, simply made but effective even for trudging through the snow. (That was revealed by a group of hikers who walked through the Alps wearing duplicates of Ötzi's shoes.) The shoes have deerskin uppers, with soles made from brown bear hide. That is a puzzle, not just because bears weren't that common in the area even when Ötzi lived, but also because bearskin doesn't wear nearly as well as cowhide, which Ötzi would have had access to. There was also an inner boot made of knotted linden fibres; the knots were extremely complex, again suggesting a fair degree

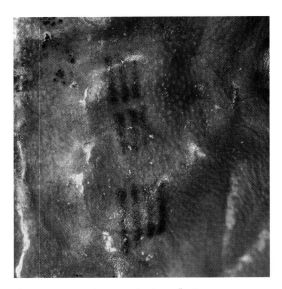

▲ For reasons that aren't clear, Ötzi was very heavily tattooed.

of sophistication. And, finally, a layer of grass provided warmth. This is the accepted view of the shoes, but a British archaeologist, Jacqui Wood, has a radically different interpretation. She thinks that Ötzi was wearing snowshoes, and that what we're calling shoes were only the upper part of those snowshoes; she has examined curved pieces of wood that others have identified as a backpack and contends that these are, in fact, the frame of his snowshoes.

Ötzi's tattoos were, for us, the most intriguing part of his story, because we were able to bring them to life—literally. A chemical analysis of his many tattoos—more than fifty of them—had shown that the coloration was produced by soot. They're simple designs, mostly parallel lines and arrays of dots, but the location is curious:

▲ His shoes, although low-tech, have been shown to be well-suited for trudging through the snow.

most are on parts of the body that wouldn't normally be seen, and many correspond to known acupuncture points, leading some to suggest that acupuncture is even older than we thought. But at *Daily Planet* we went one step further. It wasn't possible to bring Ötzi into the studio, but we did find a volunteer substitute, archaeologist Julian Siggers, now at the Royal Ontario Museum. Volunteering for what, exactly? To be tattooed just as Ötzi was!

Julian has always had an interest in ancient tools, and he'd noted that in the iceman's tool kit there was a sliver of bone that had been sharpened at one end. So he put together his own set of instruments that conceivably could have been used for tattooing thousands of years ago: a couple of tools made of bone, three made of antler, and one of stone. Julian suspected the bone would

be too soft and, given that antler has been widely used in cultures all over the world, guessed it would be better. He recruited tattoo artist Daemon Rowanchilde.

▲ Many of Ötzi's tattoos are located at acupuncture points.

Rowanchilde had always been fascinated by the human body in motion and how it could be enhanced by a well-placed and well-executed tattoo. He was already drawn to tribal designs (as opposed to motorcycles or hearts with arrows through them), and so he and Julian got down to business. It turned out that the antler wasn't that great—even though it punctured the skin well enough, the tattoo ink wasn't drawn under the skin. Nor did the stone tool work. But the bone was fantastic, a perfectly good tattoo needle, probably because it was porous. Even so, Julian had one very personal misgiving about using bone:

"It's more painful, especially initially, the first five minutes before the endorphins are released into your system. It also takes a lot longer. The tattoo was about 2 inches long but it took a couple of hours, much longer than it would have with a tattoo gun."

So Julian was permanently changed by this brush with Ötzi (or at least a couple of inches of the skin just behind his right shoulder were), but that was nothing compared to the impact on the tattoo artist, Daemon Rowanchilde. Here's what he thinks now, looking back on the experiment:

Before the tattoo experiment for which Julian was so gracious to offer his skin, I was already tattooing in a style inspired by and reminiscent of tattoos done by indigenous cultures around the world.

Compared to indigenous tattooing, I found Western tattoos to be gaudy and cartoonish, often offering little depth of meaning. Since the Iceman experiment, my style, understanding, and approach have grown and developed.

What appeals to me about the primitive tools is that they're made by hand and crafted from organic materials, and they don't make any noise other than the sound of the movement in the skin. I like things that are handmade because of the energy that goes into them when creating them. I also like my tattoo machines, but I'd love if they didn't make such a noise and have to be plugged in. I've recently switched my old coil machines to pneumatic machines, which create less noise, are lighter to hold, and are easier on the skin. There are pros and cons to both. I still tattoo people by hand sometimes upon request, but it takes longer, and the needles are made from stainless steel for health reasons. There's a certain unique quality to the experience.

The Ötzi story wouldn't be complete without reference to "the curse"! Yes, in the twenty-first-century version of King Tut's curse, seven people who were connected to Ötzi's discovery or analysis have died. They include Rainer Henn, head of the original forensic team, killed in a head-on car accident (while on his way to give a talk about Ötzi); an Austrian journalist, Rainer Hoelzl, who died shortly after participating in a documentary about Ötzi; and Dr. Tom Loy, who died in Australia just before finishing a book on Ötzi. But the most poignant was Konrad Spindler, who'd probably studied Ötzi more than any other researcher. He dismissed the curse, adding,

"You'll be saying *I* will be next." He died in April 2005.

But let's be serious here. Spindler had a chronic disease, and two of the others who died were mountaineers who lost their lives while climbing. And, of course, there are many others who've studied Ötzi and are still alive and well. Mind you, in the end they'll all be dead!

▲ ▶ Ötzi's tattoos were an inspiration to a modern tattoo artist and his archaeologist client.

THE BODY FARM

IT'S IRONIC THAT CRIME SHOWS, COMPLETE with full-on views of murder "victims" and graphic details of how they died, are among the most popular on television, and yet when the real thing is presented, entertainment slides into discomfort. Even I felt a tiny bit squeamish when we aired two stories on what's called the "Body Farm."

This is a fenced-off forest on about a hectare of land in Tennessee; its real name is the University of Tennessee's Forensic Anthropology Research Center. It is indeed a body farm: people who've willed their bodies are placed in the woods after death in a variety of positions, some clothed, some not, some half-buried, some left to decompose right on the surface, fully exposed to the elements. At any time there are thirty to forty bodies in various stages of decay. Arpad Vass, the lead scientist here, has made a career of improving the forensic techniques used to gather evidence from a corpse. He's especially interested in making estimates of the time since death more accurate.

▶ The Body Farm: final resting place of those who have donated their bodies to improve forensic knowledge.

"There are a number of methods that are used," Vass explains. "Most are most effective within the first forty-eight hours after death. The medical examiner is typically only an expert in that time frame. But after that first forty-eight-hour period, historically forensic entomology was the best means of doing time since death. That had its heyday in the 1980s."

Forensic entomology is the study of the various insect species that find a corpse and feed on it. There's a time sequence to their arrival, and by characterizing the species that are already present, it's possible to estimate how long the corpse has been there. But it's an imperfect technique, Dr. Vass says: "More recent cases have shown that individuals don't always have insects associated with them when they die. Therefore, we've developed a number of other techniques for time since death based on soft tissue decomposition." Or, to put it bluntly, rot.

It's not the idea of the Body Farm that is most challenging; it's the details. You only have to read the words that describe the various stages of decomposition—"fresh," "bloated," "decayed," and "skeletonized"— to know that. One such detail is livor mortis. Unlike the more familiar rigor mortis, when the body stiffens soon after death, livor mortis describes the pooling of blood, especially in the limbs. If a leg is pressed into the ground, pressure will force the blood out of that area, leaving it blanched. As Dr. Vass points out, if part of a limb in contact with the ground isn't blanched, that suggests that the body was moved after death. It's this connection between the often grotesque details of decomposition and the murder investigation that's the point of the Body Farm.

▲ The arrival of insects at a corpse is a useful but imperfect guide to the time of death.

▲ Even colour changes in a body can be useful clues in a murder case.

However, as decomposition proceeds, it becomes more and more difficult to find flesh and blood details that can help pin down time of death, and Dr. Vass and his colleagues have moved on to the chemical aftermath of death, specifically volatile fatty acids.

Dr. Vass describes the process: "These are organic components, that, as the body liquefies, will seep into the matrix on which the body resides, whether it's soil, bedding, carpeting, trunk liners…. If the body is clothed, they'll seep into the clothing. Once the body is removed, we can collect a small sample of the soil from under the body, and based on the ratio of these volatile fatty acids that are present, we can quite accurately determine how long this individual has been dead." In this instance, "accurately" means pinpointing death to within a day or two after a month's decomposition. Other kinds of analysis can be even more precise. Even if all that's left is bones, inorganic materials like phosphates, sulphur, calcium, and chlorides can help determine time since death within a two-week time frame for every year a body has been left outside.

As Dr. Vass's research has taken him down to the chemical residues left behind by decomposition, it has brought him closer to a different group of researchers: Glen Turpin and Brian Armstrong and their search dogs, Bosco and Jesse. They train these dogs to detect the odours of decomposition, taking advantage of the

▲ This "capture hood" collected odours released from a buried body, allowing researchers to characterize them. These are the odours that the dogs detect.

well-known fact that dogs' olfactory abilities are off the charts. But having a good nose isn't enough. Search dogs must be strongly motivated and tenacious, and so Brian and Glen prefer Belgian Malinois, a kind of sheepdog with exactly those qualities. Together, men and dogs work with the Ontario Volunteer Emergency Response Team (OVERT).

We went out with the team for a practice run in the snow, hiding bunches of gauze or handfuls of soil that had been soaked in liquids from decaying cadavers. The assortment of chemicals in the liquids is bewildering—there are maybe four hundred in all. Detecting them becomes more difficult with the depth of the grave, as decomposition changes the farther down in the soil the body lies. And judging from the dogs' reaction, the human cocktail is different from that of other mammals. But how? That's the question that links these two groups, and it's one that Arpad Vass is trying to answer.

Back on the Body Farm, we found him capturing and enumerating the chemicals released from a body that had been in a shallow grave for two and a half years. With studies like this, Dr. Vass has selected about thirty to fifty chemicals out of the four hundred that he thinks are the most relevant, because they seem to be present in all corpses and migrate up through the soil to the surface, where the dog detects them. Determining which chemicals are most important for the dog, and in what ratios, is a hugely difficult task. Yet sorting those chemicals out would not only help train the dogs more efficiently, but might also make possible a lightweight hand-held device that investigators could use in the absence of trained dogs.

Arpad Vass has developed a prototype of such a device. It's called, with an apparent tip of the hat to its canine colleagues, LABRADOR: light-weight analyzer for buried remains and decompositional odour recognition. Our dog handlers doubt that their animals are going to be put out of work by an inanimate rival any time soon, but Arpad, Brian, and Glen are all on the same page when it comes to what they do. In Arpad's words, "Everything we glean forensically from the subjects and the research will help the victims of crime, and that's really the goal here."

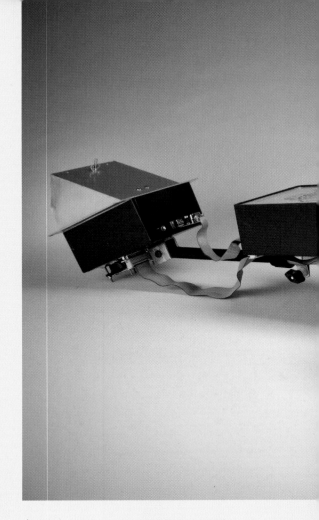

▲ LABRADOR ... the technology equivalent of the canine crew.

▶ Brian, Glen, and one of their search dogs.

JANE GOODALL, PRIMATOLOGIST, ANTHROPOLOGIST, AND UN MESSENGER OF PEACE

"Chimpanzees, like us, have a dark side to their nature. We both can show love and compassion, and sadly, chimpanzees and humans can show brutality—chimps even have behaviour somewhat like a primitive form of warfare. And I think this suggests that that kind of behaviour was present millions of years ago as part of our ancient primate heritage, when we had a common ancestor, a sort of ape-like, human-like creature.

"And there are those people who say, 'Well, if we've inherited this aggressive tendency from our ancient primate past, then war and aggression are inevitable in our own species,' but I don't agree. I think that we—more than any other living creature—have the ability to control our genes. And each one of us has a choice which of these two sides we are going to try and develop."

GOMBE, TANZANIA

All I can say is that it was a lot cooler taking the boat from Kigoma to Jane Goodall's Gombe than it was following Patti the chimp and her offspring through the jungle the next day. Patti had a reputation for leading trackers on wild goose chases and avoiding paths at all costs, and we found out just how true that was. My cameraman, Mike Heenan, earned his money that day, crawling through the Gombe underbrush with a camera on his shoulder. It was just another day for Patti, but an amazing experience for us.

A SHRIMP WITH A BITE

THE MANTIS SHRIMP IS NOT WELL named—it's neither a mantis nor a shrimp. But a bad name is its only shortcoming. It is a large crustacean (it can be a foot long, or 30 centimetres), but even that's not its claim to fame. It is a fearsome predator, and it kills its prey by unleashing something that has no equivalent anywhere else in the living world: an arm-like appendage that swings out at unbelievable speeds and literally smashes its target.

Let's put some real numbers to this. Dr. Sheila Patek at the University of Massachusetts and her colleagues have been studying this beast for years, and here are some of the calculations they've come up with. The smasher is normally tucked in under the animal's head, but when it's released, it accelerates at roughly the same rate a bullet does when it leaves the muzzle of a gun. And it gets up to a speed of 80 kilometres per hour in just

▶ This snail has just been smashed by one of the most powerful weapons in nature. The pieces of shell floating away testify to that.

a little more than a couple of thousandths of a second, 50 times faster than the blink of an eye. It's not a big surprise that, as far as anyone can tell, this movement is one of the fastest in the animal world. Trap-jaw ants are faster (their jaws close at about 230 kilometres per hour), but as Dr. Patek pointed out to *Daily Planet,* it's a lot harder to overcome the drag forces of water than of air, so the mantis shrimp still stands proud.

Speed is one thing, but crushing force is what the shrimp really needs in order to disable or kill its prey, and it can certainly deliver blows like that. Large mantis shrimp have even been known to crack aquarium glass, so it's no wonder that divers call them "thumb splitters." Their predators, including octopuses, are very, very careful to seize the mantis shrimp in a way that directs the hammer blow harmlessly away.

▶ One of the few photos in existence that proves a mantis shrimp can shatter the glass of its aquarium.

Not even Dr. Evil could come up with something so brilliantly destructive. How can something so diabolical be created from living tissue?

But Dr. Patek's lab has discovered that the killing force delivered by this animal is not even as straightforward as the crushing impact of a fast-moving, hard-shelled body part. It *is* all that, but it's also something much more insidious.

When the arm accelerates with killing force, it creates severe disturbances in the water. The velocity is so great that so-called cavitation bubbles are formed, a little like the bubbles of boiling water. These bubbles almost instantaneously implode, releasing huge amounts of energy in the form of a shock wave—so much energy, in fact, that they generate light, sound, and force. That force means that the shrimp's initial strike is followed almost immediately by a blow from the imploding bubbles. That the bubbles have great potential for damage may be seen in the surface of the shrimp's own appendage, which over time becomes dented and pitted. Of course, the animal has an answer for this: moult every few months to create a shiny, smooth new striker. Not even Dr. Evil could come up with something so brilliantly destructive.

How can something so diabolical be created from living tissue? This has been one of the main focuses of the Patek lab, where painstaking work with computer modelling, scanning, and high-speed video has revealed how it all works. Sheer muscle power can't account for the shrimp's brute force, because the energy has to be released much more quickly than a muscle is capable of. Instead, the shrimp has to store the energy of the contraction of its major arm muscles in some sort of spring, prevent the bounce-back of that spring by a latch, and then instantly release the latch. I was heartened at first when researchers thought they might have narrowed down the spring mechanism to a small, saddle-shaped device, the technical term for which is a *hyperbolic paraboloid*. A Canadian connection! The roof of Calgary's Pengrowth Saddledome is still considered the world's longest-spanning concrete hyperbolic paraboloid. Unfortunately, while it's true that the mantis shrimp is the only animal that uses a hyperbolic paraboloid (its saddle) as a powerful spring to store energy, its contribution to the total energy stored for the claw is pretty small. Most of the energy from flexing muscle(s) is held in other, more rigid structures nearby.

▲ The one hyperbolic paraboloid that most Canadians are familiar with.

The complexity of all this is somewhat staggering, although in principle the shrimp's makeup reminds me of a similarly deadly weapon that classmates and I used to fiddle around with in elementary school. I won't reveal its exact design (in the interests of protecting those foolish enough to try to use it, not to mention their targets), but it involved taking a common bobby pin and manipulating it so that a gradually applied force could be stored in the pin and released instantaneously only when a latch-like mechanism was triggered. The

movement—a mere blur of a downward, swinging motion—was even reminiscent of the mantis shrimp's appendage. The bobby pin couldn't break aquarium glass, but it could, when applied properly, draw human blood.

But that was for amusement—admittedly perverse—and nothing more. The mantis shrimp has used such fundamental engineering principles as springs, latches, and levers to evolve a weapon without peer. But why? What is it about the environment of this creature through millions of years that facilitated the development of something so specialized? It does prey on hard-shelled creatures, like snails, some of which have shells that might defy even a hammer-wielding human. Is the additional impact of the bubble implosion just a lucky evolutionary fluke, inevitable on the heels of such a powerful strike? There are other species of shrimp that snap a claw to create cavitation bubbles to stun and kill their prey, but these animals don't combine this skill with a killing blow—only mantis shrimp do that.

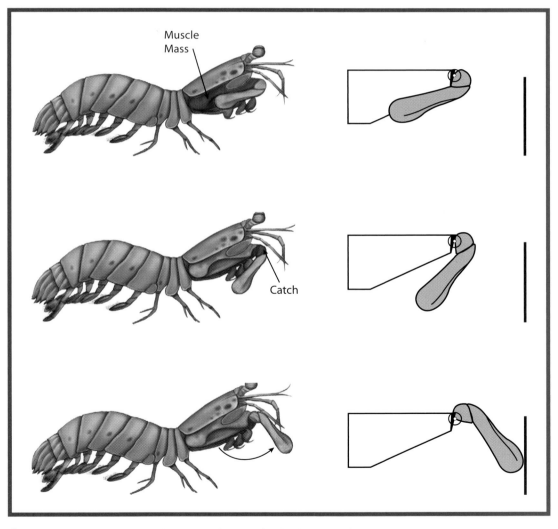

▲ How the incredible mantis shrimp smasher is unleashed.

TREE FROGS

THE RED-EYED TREE FROG IS A POSTER species if there ever was one. But the striking adult gives no hint of how harrowing its early life was. This is a species that owes its life to an extraordinary ability to sense danger—when it's an embryo!

Red-eyed tree frogs live in damp forests in Central and South America. Unlike their North American relatives, these frogs lay their eggs not *in* the water, but on leaves overhanging it, because their egg masses simply can't get access to enough oxygen if they're flooded with water. But while being in the water would ensure an early death for frog embryos, being attached to the surface of a leaf is no picnic either. There they are exposed to predatory insects, as well as to a much greater threat: tree-climbing snakes. Snakes will make very short work of a frog egg mass if they happen upon one, and in some snake-rich areas, 20 percent of all frogs' eggs could be consumed.

▶ You would never know just how hazardous is the early life of this poster-child frog.

Normally the frogs will hatch six or seven days after the eggs are deposited on the leaf—an awfully long time to be exposed. But the embryonic frogs have an amazing strategy for survival: when a snake begins to tear away and swallow the eggs on one side of an egg mass, embryos in the other eggs begin to hatch prematurely and plummet into the water below. It's absolutely mind-boggling to see. The gluttony of the snake is disturbing and violent, but the speed with which the unhatched embryos respond is astonishing. For the first little while the egg mass shakes and twists as the reptile gorges itself, but then embryos inside the as-yet undisturbed eggs begin to twitch and turn, and tadpoles start falling, first one or two, then half a dozen, then more, all in a desperate attempt to escape.

And *desperate* is the right word, because even if an immature tadpole hatches in time, it faces new challenges. It has entered the water while not yet fully developed, and it usually lacks the swimming ability to avoid the whole new set of predators that it then encounters. Now you might think it must still be better to take a chance than condemn yourself to certain death by remaining in the egg mass. And if that were all there was to it, you'd be right. But there's more.

How do the unhatched frogs know that the snake is attacking them? They feel the shaking and vibration of the entire egg mass as the snake begins to dismantle it. (This has been confirmed in the lab by vibrating the eggs and watching them hatch.) Somehow, and the details are not fully understood, that vibration triggers early hatching. But this is more complicated than it might seem. The environment in which the red-eyed tree frog lives is wet—heavy rains are common. Heavy rainfalls also shake the leaves and their egg masses, probably more often than do the snakes. But if the frog embryos pushed the panic button in response to those vibrations, they'd be risking their lives in the water unnecessarily. So to maximize their chances of survival, they have to be able to tell the difference.

Biologist Karen Warkentin at Boston University has been carefully teasing out the differences—and similarities—between the two types of signals, and she's found that frogs' eggs do everything they can to distinguish between snakes and raindrops. Some features of the vibrations aren't useful at all. Strength or force of vibration is one: both rain and snakes can bounce the egg mass back and forth with equal strength. The speed of the shaking—its frequency—is a better piece of information, because snake-induced vibrations are generally lower in frequency, but even here there's lots of overlap, because rain can be strong at the low frequencies as well.

Timing is something else: rain tends to create short bursts of vibration separated by brief intervals, the shortest ever recorded in fact. The longest pauses between vibrations happen during a reptile attack, when the snake is forced to pause to swallow the eggs already in its mouth. It's clear that the embryonic frogs somehow take all these features into account and weigh the relative importance of each, then act—or not. Relying on any single clue would be a big mistake.

In the lab Dr. Warkentin has seen that high frequencies (typical of rain), even in the presence of the low, threatening frequencies of snakes, reduce hatching, so the embryos are taking both into account. Yet she has seen snake attacks in the jungle during rainstorms, so how the embryos weigh all that contradictory evidence is puzzling.

There's one other clue that this is exactly what they're doing, though: it takes an embryo only about a second to hatch, but the first hatches in response to a snake attack don't begin until it has already been underway for at least sixteen seconds, and continue for another four minutes. If they aren't weighing the evidence, then acting, why the delay?

After seeing how all this information is apparently successfully processed and used to make a hatch/no hatch decision, it's easy to forget that these aren't adult frogs, or even tadpoles—they're embryos, embryos making tough survival decisions. Not so long ago, no one would have thought any of this was possible.

▲ This snake will not get to eat all these eggs—check out the early-hatching tadpole at the bottom.

HARRY MEETS SALLY

IN THE MOVIE *WHEN HARRY MET SALLY,* that meeting was, well, hot. But here we're talking very, very hot—and that's just Harry himself. He's definitely hot all right, but not in the usual sense. Harry Burns is his name, and burning is exactly what he does. He works for the University of Alberta's Protective Clothing and Equipment Research Facility; in fact, he donates his time as an electronic flash-fire mannequin. You could call him a scientific stuntman, because he stands in for all those real people whose jobs expose them to the risks of sudden fires and serious burns.

As you can see, Harry's still in pretty good shape for a guy whose body is routinely engulfed in flames—except for that pole through his head. Mechanical engineer Mark Ackerman assured us that wasn't the result of an industrial accident; the pole is actually the conduit for the information that Harry transmits as he's being flamed. Harry has 110 sensors built right into his "skin," and they give a detailed picture of just how well—or not—protective clothing would work on a real human.

◄ Harry Burns is ... HOT! This electronic flash-fire mannequin stands in harm's way every day to test protective clothing and equipment.

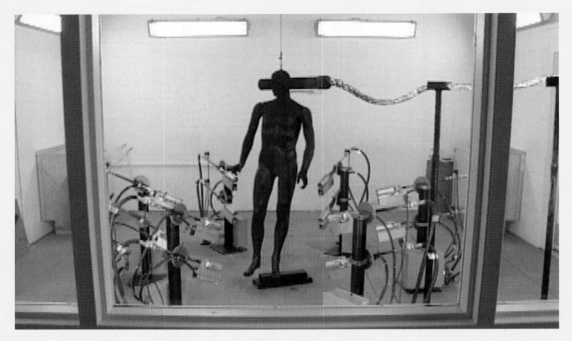

▲ Surrounded by propane torches capable of 800°C heat: just another day at the office for Harry.

When we visited the lab Harry was testing a Nomex, a flame-resistant type of nylon and cousin to Kevlar (not as strong, but incredibly flame-resistant). Dressed as carefully as royalty by his researchers, Harry stood calmly as he was blasted by a dozen good-sized propane torches. Mark describes the inferno as "a ball of flame with a temperature of about 800 degrees Celsius; in heat flux terms, which we use, that's something like 80 kilowatts per square metre—about eighty times the level you'd see in bright sunlight."

As startling as it is to see a human figure absolutely engulfed in flames, the real juice of the experiment is on the computer screen: an outline image of Harry with coloured patches on it, showing which areas of Harry's body had sustained the worst burns and which had been protected. A pink square represents a second-degree burn; a red patch, third-degree. A few burns are scattered over Harry's body, not for the first time. A typical Harry might endure something like two thousand burns over his lifetime, and when fatigue sets in, Son of Harry steps in. The researchers are working on their fourth Harry now.

And Harry's offspring are leaving the country. One has gone to Texas to take the flames in tests of fires from gas leaks, and another is just settling in at Donkook University in Korea.

▶ Somewhere in that mass of flame is Harry, trying on a new wardrobe.

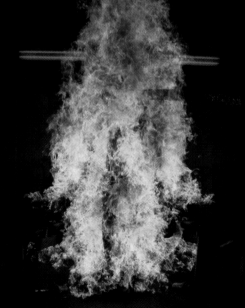

And then there's Sally: Sally's an Aussie, and she's realistic. The North American female mannequins that Mark checked out tended to be over 6 feet tall and have extremely tiny, unrealistic, Barbie-like waists. It's not that Aussie Sally is unattractive though. Why, she even has the giant bar through her head. Harry, meet Sally.

TIM FLANNERY, PALEONTOLOGIST AND ENVIRON- MENTALIST

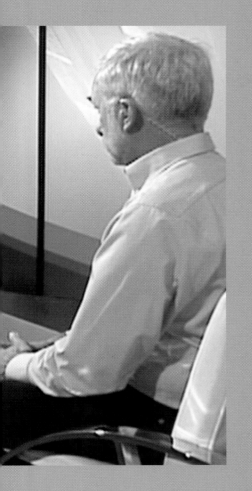

"The biggest issue for me, and the one that is the most poorly understood, is the way that earth's natural systems draw down carbon dioxide and keep the earth in chemical balance. Plants draw down 8 percent of all atmospheric carbon dioxide every year. So you can imagine that if there were no new carbon dioxide going into the atmosphere, in twelve years there'd be no carbon dioxide in the atmosphere at all.

"The way I put it is that plants represent the best carbon capture mechanism you could ever ask for. What we've got to do is enhance the storage capacity for that carbon. And we do that by protecting forests, by making agricultural practices more sustainable, fighting desertification, tree planting, all of that sort of stuff. It strengthens the life-force of the planet."

SEVEN

Extraordinary Science

In the end, it's always about ideas, isn't it? And those ideas can play in realms impossibly distant from one another. Stand where an artist once stood, supply an artist with a sense he never had, or mash art and science together to spoof our dependence on electronic communication. It's all science; it's all extraordinary.

IT'S A SOUND
OF RED

NEIL HARBISSON IS AN ARTIST WHO SEES the world in a way no other artist does. Neil can see only shades of grey: no colour. He spent his childhood memorizing the colours of things, but never actually saw what he was talking about, and ultimately became frustrated by the fact that grass isn't always green, the sky isn't always blue.

Today Neil is able to perceive the differences among colours and shades. But he doesn't see them—he hears them. Neil has a device, the Eye-Borg, that translates the frequencies of light around him into tones of different pitches—well, not exactly *all* the sounds around him. He has to bring the light-gathering unit close to the coloured surface. The higher the tone, the hotter the colour: reds are low tones, greens intermediate, and blues and purples the highest. Following Neil down the street as he looks at his greys and whites, then listens to them, is a strange

▶ Neil pays attention to colour not with his eyes, but with his ears.

232

experience: "If I listen to this medium-grey, it sounds very low so it's actually a shade of red…. This next wall looks dirty white, but it sounds a bit higher than red so it's in the range of yellow."

The tones aren't particularly evocative, and it's hard to imagine what it's like for Neil to be aware that there are certain colours around him but be unable to experience them. He admits that this was always frustrating, and even now that he can "hear" colours, he still feels he has a love-hate relationship with them. But his world is changed, there's no doubt, and much of the credit is due to Adam Montandon of HMC Interactive.

Adam explains, "At HMC we try to do the most amazing things with new technology, whether it's unusual, magical, surprising, something that makes people say, 'Wow.'" And that's exactly what they did for Neil. They created a technology to turn light into sound.

"It's very simple," Adam tells me. "We use a head-mounted camera, similar to a normal webcam, a regular laptop, a PC, and a pair of headphones. The camera looks at the colour in front of it, then slows down that colour so that it stops becoming visual and starts becoming sound, then plays that sound back to Neil so that he can hear it."

Of course, it's not quite that simple: the Eye-Borg is actually transforming the electromagnetic waves of light into the compressions of sound. But if Adam claims that's simple, who's going to argue?

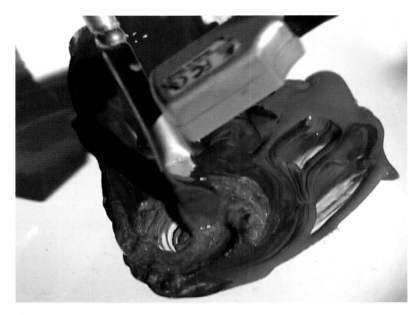

▲ Listening to blue-green.

▲ Neil's work is unique, the product of an artist who both sees and hears what he paints.

Even though the Eye-Borg works best as a close-focus instrument, it still allows Neil to experience the average colour of a room, whether warm or cold. It's not the complete experience of synaesthesia, but Neil has found that the technology works both ways: colours make sounds, and sounds make colours. "For example, my Hoover sounds red, although I know it's actually blue. The telephone line sounds green." It also makes a new kind of art possible: Neil is painting the capital cities of Europe as panels of colour representing the overall sounds of the cities. He walks the streets of each neighbourhood until he feels he's perceived the main colour(s) of that city.

Both the Eye-Borg and Neil will continue to change: Neil in how he wants to use it, and even reprogram it for different experiences, and the technology itself. Already it has a much fuller colour spectrum than it did at first, and Adam Montandon foresees a time when people with perfectly normal vision might want to try the Eye-Borg themselves, for fun or to create new works of art.

But that's the future—already the Eye-Borg has changed Neil Harbisson's life: "After a few months of wearing it I began to feel that the eye was part of my body. I began to find it strange to take it off because I was wearing it all the time—it just became an extra sense."

And that, my friends, is the definition of a cyborg.

PEOPLE WE'VE MET

RAY KURZWEIL, INVENTOR, SCIENTIST, AND FUTURIST

"In my view we'll have robots—artificial intelligence at human levels—that have the subtlety of our pattern recognition by 2029. That's really the heart of human intelligence: we're very good at recognizing patterns. Machines are getting better at that as well, and the broad subtlety and suppleness where we can go from topic to topic, use different types of reasoning fluidly—machines will achieve that by the end of the 2020s. But in my view it's not going to be an alien invasion of intelligent machines competing with us—we're actually going to merge with this technology, it's going to go inside our bodies and brains in the form of nanobots, blood cell–sized robots. They'll ultimately go inside the capillaries of our brains, interact with our biological neurons, and actually expand human intelligence."

ANTS IN A PANIC

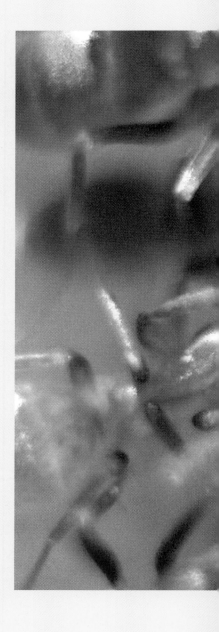

IF YOU HAVE A COUPLE OF HUNDRED ants in a dish in the lab, and you pump in a noxious gas, the ants will panic and try to escape. While we can't know exactly what's going on in their so-called minds, it *looks* like panic: they start running around, picking up the larvae, and trying to escape. Even the queen, who's usually pretty sedentary, runs for it. This sounds like some cruel adolescent boys' delight, but in the hands of Dr. Martin Burd, it's an experiment to see if there are better ways of handling human emergencies.

Emergencies like the fatal crush of people in a theatre fire, or a crowd pressing against the barriers at an outdoor concert. Dr. Burd is a biologist at Australia's Monash University, and one time in South America, he explains, his interest in ant behaviour led him unexpectedly to humans: "I was looking at the ant trails when I suddenly felt as if I were in a helicopter looking down on a highway below, giving the morning traffic report. I was

▶ Ants may not think their way out of a jam, but maybe we don't either.

▲ Martin Burd finds crowds very, very interesting.

looking down and thinking, 'Those ants look like people,' and it was then that the correspondence between the crowd movements of ants and the crowd movement of people hit me." Ever since, Burd has had a foot in two camps: the behaviour of ants, and the behaviour of humans in crowds.

If we could understand how such crowds work, we might be able to lessen their risk, but that understanding is hard to come by. It's difficult to re-create actual disasters: survivors of the real thing can't—or refuse to—remember exactly what happened or what they thought. Such accounts are too chaotic and uncontrolled. And Dr. Burd

says that the usual preferred alternative, the controlled experiment, isn't all that great either: "You can get volunteers into a room, say, 'When I blow the whistle, everyone rush for the door and pretend it's a fire,' and you can get some data on human movement in that way. But you can never be sure that people are acting and reacting in exactly the way they would if they really thought their lives were in danger, say, if there were a fire in the building."

So if you can't observe the real thing, controlled or uncontrolled, the next-best approach is to model crowd behaviour. Traditionally computers have treated crowds as if they were masses of particles flowing back and forth like a fluid, but because that approach doesn't really allow any individuality (which is what crowds are all about), more advanced programs were created. These gave the individual particles some options, so they didn't always have to flow with the crowd. Such programs have come up with unexpected conclusions, like the fact that panicking, speeding pedestrians can clog up an exit that they would have moved through with

no delay if only they'd kept to their normal walking speed.

Then there was a surprise prediction about the effect of a partial obstruction of an exit. Dr. Burd explains, "It's been suggested that having a column in front of an exit can actually improve the flow of people out that doorway, especially in an emergency, but it's completely counterintuitive. You wouldn't expect that having a semi-obstruction in front of a doorway is going to improve things."

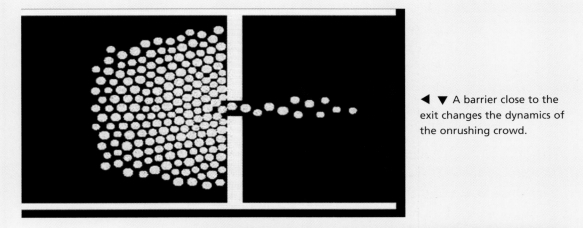

◀ ▼ A barrier close to the exit changes the dynamics of the onrushing crowd.

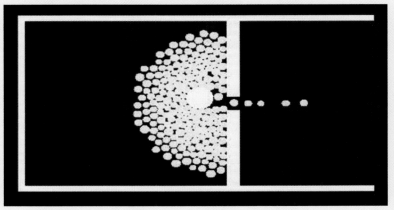

No kidding! Block the exit so you can increase the flow of traffic through it? That was the claim, but how to test it in some way other than just programming another computer? Martin Burd turned to his ants: "The beauty of using ants as a model is that we can genuinely panic them, and obviously we can't do those sorts of experiments with humans."

That last part makes sense, but can the behaviour of ants really tell us something useful about ourselves? The results of Burd's experiments suggest it does. One hundred ants unimpeded by an obstruction needed fifty-six seconds to clear their dish when gassed; the same number forced to move around a column took only thirty-three seconds.

"The idea," Dr. Burd elaborates, "is that when people are crowding around a doorway they literally touch each other and exert pressure, so by having an obstruction there, you essentially prevent those sorts of high-density groups with strong pressure from forming around an exitway, and thus the passage of people can be smoother and more coherent."

So the ants back up the computer programs, and both suggest that what we expect from a crowd, and what we actually get, can be two very different things. It just goes to show that while we *are* thinking creatures, important parts of our behaviour are simple enough to be mimicked—even by ants.

▲ The barrier prevents little knots of ants forming near the exit and slowing things down.

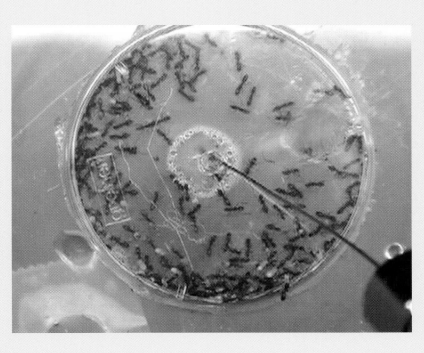

◄ The busy but peaceful colony …

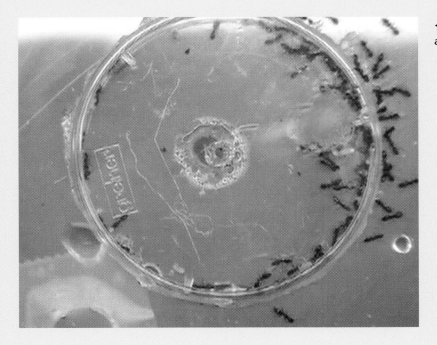

◄ … is thrown into a panic by the gas.

E.O. WILSON,
BIOLOGIST
AND
CONSERVATIONIST
AUTHOR

"We depend far more than most people realize on the continued existence, health, and diversity of what I like to call 'the little things that run the earth'—that is, the bugs, the fungi, the roundworms, and all these things that you have to put under a microscope even to be able to look at carefully. They're there making the soil, purifying the water, playing a major role in creating the very atmosphere we breathe.

"A study made in 1997 by a group of economists and biologists tried to put a figure on all the services we are getting from these natural environments and all the creatures living in them. They came up with a figure of 33 *trillion* dollars."

THE GREAT TOMATO EXPERIMENT

ONE OF *DAILY PLANET*'S MOST IMAGINATIVE and exciting stories came early in our fifteen years, in 1996, when we investigated the power of prayer and healing with the Great Tomato Experiment. In the mid-1990s there was great interest in trying to scientifically establish, and put some firm numbers to, the validity of such alternative approaches to medicine. In fact, at the time of the tomato experiment, data suggested that interventions like therapeutic touch (which involves a practitioner manipulating a patient's energy field, usually without actually touching him or her) had some demonstrable effect. But the small number of studies like this were not enough to overcome the prevailing view, especially among scientists, that something as physically improbable and biologically undetectable as an aura or spirit that could be manipulated by thought was simply imaginary.

◀ On the left, the victim; on the right, the pathogen. But can human thoughts stave off infection?

"I don't know that there's much of a difference between dealing with tomatoes and dealing with humans. For me the bigger question is, What's the intent? And when I go into my work my intent is to heal, to send love."

This subject was so hotly debated and controversial that we felt we just had to jump in, and thus was born the experiment. Here's how it worked: with the gracious (though skeptical) assistance of the head of the University of Toronto botany department, Dr. Verna Higgins, and her colleagues, we created nine groupings of seven tomatoes apiece. Six of the nine sets were infected with a common tomato fungus, *Colletotrichum coccodes*—it causes a fairly common disease called anthracnose of tomato, a spreading, darkening, bruise-like lesion on the tomato's skin. Each tomato was inoculated with great care to ensure that the small plug of fungus and the depth to which it was inserted were the same for all forty-two that were treated. The remaining three sets had their skins broken, but no fungus was inoculated—they served as controls to ensure that subsequent damage and spoilage would be due to the inoculated fungus alone.

But all attention was focused on the tomatoes that had been infected. They were going to be put in cupboards for the next week, but before that, on the Friday morning that the experiment began, we invited a group of seven healers into the lab. Their task was to concentrate on the tomatoes in three of the bins and try to prevent the spread of the fungus during that week of storage by "distant mental imaging." The participants were allowed to look at them, try to feel their aura, do whatever they had to do to get in sync with the tomatoes, but they weren't allowed to touch either the bins or the tomatoes themselves. Once the tomatoes were put away for the seven-day incubation period, the healers would have no access to them.

There were seven healers in all, people who'd been trained in therapeutic touch, energy healing, and reflexology, among them a pair of nurses, a physician, a social worker, and a businessman. It's fair to say they recognized that there were challenges to trying to connect with a vegetable (sorry, a *fruit*), but they were definitely up to the task, even feeling a certain amount of confidence, according to a few healers:

"All of a sudden I got a very strong whiff of delicious-smelling fragrance of tomatoes, and instantly I got the sense that they're like tiny little babies in an isolette—very vulnerable, very willing to be loved and helped and supported."

"I don't know that there's much of a difference between dealing with tomatoes and dealing with humans. For me the bigger question is, What's the intent? And when I go into my work my intent is to heal, to send love."

Some were more cautious: "The ultimate goal would be to have the tomato

▲ The data was clean, unambiguous, and dead certain.

completely healed from the blight. I don't think that's quite possible, but I think we might slow it down and give these tomatoes a better chance. It'll be interesting—I'm looking forward to seeing how it turns out."

The seven healers were actually just the tip of the iceberg. We invited all our viewers to think about the tomatoes, and to help accomplish that, we showed images of the tomatoes every day on the show and even on our website (that sounds pretty mundane, but don't forget this was 1996!).

A week later we brought the tomatoes out of storage and an expert examined them, measuring the size of the wound on each caused by the spreading fungus. The results were analyzed statistically, and unfortunately for those who'd hoped that remote mental imaging might have saved a tomato or two, there was no significant difference between the tomatoes that had been targeted by the healers and those that had been ignored. In fact, statistics aside, there was practically no difference at all: the average size of the lesions on controls was 31.8 millimetres; on tomatoes that the healers had focused on, it was 31.9 millimetres. It should be added that all measurements were performed blind—that is, the person doing the measurements had no idea which tomatoes were controls and which weren't.

So the results were clearly negative: there was no evidence whatsoever that distant mental imaging had had an effect. But one negative experiment doesn't mean that such techniques *never* work (although to date there's scant evidence that they do). It always troubled me that in our experiment there might have been some dastardly people in our audience who tried to hex the tomatoes, rather than heal them, and enough people like that might have overwhelmed the positive effects.

We followed up by talking to Dr. Bernard Grad about the experiment. In the 1960s, when he was a biologist at McGill University, Dr. Grad had performed some fascinating experiments with a "healer" that seemed to show that both animals and plants could respond to the mere touch— or even the energy—of such a person. He pointed out that experimenting with healing in a lab is an artificial situation to begin with, and that for some healers, working with tomatoes might not provide enough motivation. But he was intrigued that one bin of tomatoes chosen by the healers did show less damage, although this result was washed out when the bins were averaged. Overall, though, he felt that the Great Tomato Experiment was worthwhile. And so did we.

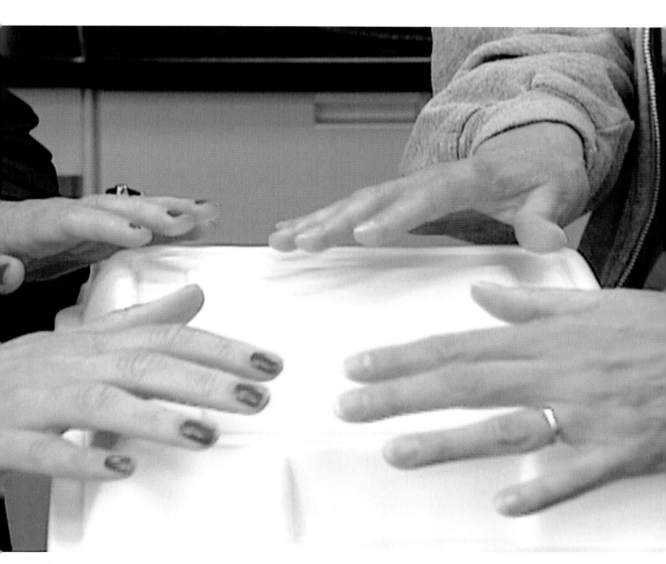

▲ The healers were this close to the tomatoes only once—on Day 1 of the experiment.

CANOE LAKE

IVAN SEMENIUK HAS PRODUCED MANY astronomy stories for *Daily Planet* over the years, introducing our audience to the visual wonders of the universe. By contrast, early in the twentieth century, the Canadian painter Tom Thomson captured on canvas the wild beauty of Algonquin Park. And yet, as distant as the two were in time, one chance event brought them together and created, for Ivan, a great astronomical adventure.

In 2003 at a Toronto exhibit of paintings by Thomson and his colleagues, Ivan was drawn to a small canvas, a sketch in oils really, called *Northern Lights*. Thomson had painted it in the spring of 1917, mere months before his mysterious drowning. What caught Ivan's eye was that the painting clearly depicted, in addition to a spectacular display of the aurora borealis, the well-known constellation Cassiopeia, a W-shaped arrangement of stars that circles the North Star as the seasons change.

That Thomson had included Cassiopeia suggested to Ivan that the artwork might represent a real scene, painted from a real location.

▶ Tom Thomson's *Northern Lights.*

Thomson was not one to depict imaginary places. Ivan's idea, in turn, provoked an exciting challenge: could he find the spot from which Thomson had painted *Northern Lights*? Even though Ivan was sure that Thomson had painted it somewhere in Algonquin Park, he still had a lot of investigative work to do.

Using a computer program to rewind the night sky, Ivan found that you'd have to be looking north-northwest to see Cassiopeia as Thomson had painted it—but when? The constellation can assume that position at different times of the night from November through April. But Thomson didn't paint in the winter, and that left only April.

"This was good news. During April there's still a lot of ice on the water in Algonquin Park and it's hard to get around. So Thomson worked close to his home base at Canoe Lake. As it turned out, there's an account of him painting northern lights there, in the spring of 1917."

That account placed Thomson on a point of land near a cabin on the lake, but which cabin, and which point, no one knew. So Ivan's task was clear: go to Canoe Lake and see if he could find a place where the horizon matched the painting. Easy to say, but considering that water levels and forest cover had changed dramatically since Thomson's time, not so easy to accomplish.

▲ The position of Cassiopeia in the sky convinced Ivan that Thomson was looking north-northwest.

▲ What looks like a line of low hills in the background of Thomson's painting is actually part of the northern lights display. The actual horizon is shown here as the yellow line. From this viewpoint at Canoe Lake today the horizon looks the same.

In Thomson's time the painter would have taken the train to the little town of Mowat, but the train station and the lumberjack's quarters where Thomson would have stayed are long gone, so Ivan, keeping in mind that Thomson painted *Northern Lights* within walking distance from them, had to be guided via backroads to where they used to be. By then his search had been dramatically narrowed down: there were only two points of land in that area with a north-northwest view.

The first wasn't a match. One chance left. To get to the second, Ivan and his guide, park naturalist Chris Boettger, had to bushwhack past some remains of the buildings of Mowat, but when they emerged from the woods, there it was: the horizon profile and Thomson's painting were nearly a perfect match.

Ivan's discovery was a thrilling piece of detective work that applied science to art, while avoiding the common pitfall of diminishing the art. Instead, Tom Thomson's *Northern Lights* now has that little extra connection to our world today: a slope of rock on the shores of Canoe Lake, where the great painter captured an astronomical moment.

LUNENBURG

ST. JOHN'S ANGLICAN CHURCH IN Lunenburg, Nova Scotia, is the second-oldest Protestant church in Canada—it was built in 1754. But on Halloween night in 2001 it was consumed by fire in what is thought to have been a prank that got badly out of hand. The event shocked the community, but the parishioners made the bold decision to rebuild, sticking as closely as possible to the original design. This was a huge challenge, especially when it came to the ceiling.

Margaret Coolen and her daughter Julie-Jayne, of Era Studio, were chosen to re-create the interior of the church, and while there was adequate photographic evidence of what the church had looked like, they came across one significant puzzle. Above the altar had been a star-studded night sky panorama, something referred to as a "mariner's sky," but Margaret Coolen thought there was something more to the stars than that: "If you were putting them up there randomly, they'd be in more of an evenly spaced pattern. They were in clumps of stars, and we thought there might be something here."

▶ The newly revitalized St. John's Anglican Church is a glorious celebration of the past—and a salute to modern scientific detective work.

256

▶ Margaret Coolen wondered about those stars …

▼ … her daughter, Julie-Jayne, re-created them.

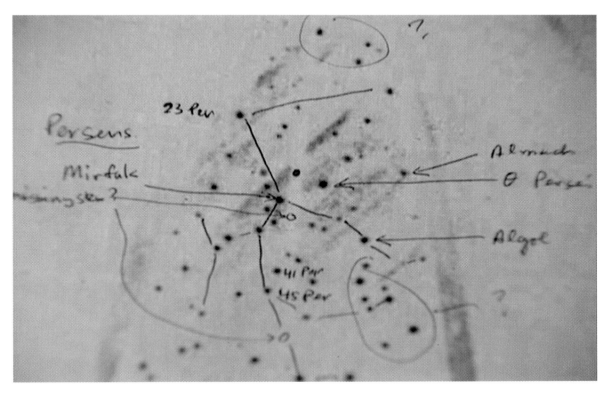

The handwritten labels on the image read: "Perseus", "Mirfak", "missing star?", "23 Per", "41 Per", "45 Per", "Almach", "θ Persei", "Algol", "?"

▲ It took a little time, but eventually David Turner's experienced astronomer's eye picked the constellation Perseus out from a wild mix of stars.

Were these stars just random splashes of paint, or did their pattern have some significance? They had apparently been painted sometime around 1900, but the scene was difficult to analyze, partly because it was incomplete: nothing that would have been obscured by the church walls or the rafters above had been included.

But if these were indeed constellations, they didn't look like any Margaret was familiar with. She needed an astronomy expert, so she took the images of the ceiling to David Turner at St. Mary's University in Halifax. At first, he says, he wasn't impressed: "It's just a horribly bland star scene, and I can imagine someone looking at it and thinking that there's nothing here to see; it looks like someone has just thrown stars up there at random."

But star patterns run deep in an astronomer's brain, and it wasn't long before something clicked with Dr. Turner. He identified the constellation Perseus, yet as he did so he realized why it had resisted identification: it appeared high in the eastern sky, a place where it never appears today. During the

"The stars represent sunset on the first Christmas as seen by people who would be living in Lunenburg, and in fact viewing it through the church rafters of the chapel."

DR. DAVID TURNER

day the earth's rotation causes this constellation to circle the north celestial pole, as marked by Polaris, the North Star. When Perseus is in the east, it's always close to the horizon, not high up.

So now, rather than being solved, the mystery was heightened. Why Perseus, and why there? But Dr. Turner was just getting warmed up. He had worked on planetarium programs about the Christmas Star, and inspired by that, set the star software to the night sky as it would have appeared over Bethlehem on the night, according to Biblical tradition, that Christ was born. The view still wasn't quite right, but one more tweak did it: he adjusted the scene so that instead of the night sky as it appeared over Bethlehem, it showed the same night as seen from Lunenburg. And everything fell into place, according to Dr. Turner:

"The stars represent sunset on the first Christmas as seen by people who would be living in Lunenburg, and in fact viewing it through the church rafters of the chapel."

All in all, a nice piece of detective work. But one piece of this puzzle is still unanswered: who did it, and more important, how? If the painting was done in 1900, the artist might have had access to the design of similar church ceilings, especially in Europe, but still would have had to know something about astronomy, to be able to transform those scenes to a Nova Scotian perspective. Star charts would have made that possible, but David Turner says, "I have great respect for the person who laid out the original design. There was an awful lot of hard work there."

Add to that the twenty-first-century hard work of astronomers and some dedicated painters, and you have, once again, the Christmas night sky over Lunenburg.

▲ The Christmas night sky, as seen from Lunenburg.

REAL SNAIL MAIL

APPARENTLY THE TERM *SNAIL MAIL* was first uttered in January 1981 by Jim Rutt, who was, and has been ever since, hugely successful in computer science, the study of complexity, and much more. Little did he know that thirty years later we'd still be dissing the postal service using his rhyming pair. But not everyone interprets it as an insult. Vicky Isley and Paul Smith, founders of boredomresearch in England, loved the concept of snail mail but wanted to make it a reality. So they did.

They created the project RealSnailMail at Bournemouth University. Real snails—eight *Helix aspersa,* the common garden snail of the UK—were tagged with 20-millimetre-wide radio frequency identification (RFID) chips. Two RFID readers, a pickup and a

◀ Either these snails are oblivious to the message they're supposed to be sending or they're behaving exactly as they should. Or both.

dispatch, were located inside the snail tank, about 50 centimetres (20 inches or so) apart. If you sent an email through the system, it would first sit at the pickup reader until a snail happened by (within 5 centimetres, or about 2 inches), then you'd wait until the snail happened to pass close by the dispatch reader at the other end of the tank. At that point, your email would be sent.

When we talked to Vicky the project was in the "good news, bad news" phase. On the one hand it had just started, and they were doing pretty well with deliveries. After four weeks they'd already had thirty-six emails picked up and delivered. On the other, there were nine thousand emails in line waiting to be picked up. And the future looked even bleaker. Well, bleaker to anyone who likes speed, that is. But to Vicky, that's not the point:

"We were asked to do a proposal in October 2006 using RFID technology. And we saw that other artists were using it in the way it was used every day—for speed—and we wanted to reverse that trend completely and use the technology in the most inefficient possible way we could." Even with that resolve, they've had trouble resisting the lure of speed. Almost all the improvements that have been considered for the system would speed it up (like smearing the RFID stations with beer to attract the snails). But Vicky and Paul would soon realize their error:

"Wait—this is supposed to be as inefficient as possible."

And really, how inefficient is that?

"Agent 010, who's also known as Beatrice, is doing really well. She's delivered six messages, so she's the top performer at the moment. They all seem to take an average of about six or seven days. So pretty much, we're averaging one message a day."

That seemed encouraging to me, but remember that backlog of nine thousand emails? Had I wanted to send a message that day, it might have reached its destination in just under twenty-five years.

Despite the absurdity, the experiment forces you to answer an interesting question: What message would you send to someone if you really had no idea when they might receive it? It could take weeks or even years. It might never arrive. What would you say?

▶ This is Beatrice, the most efficient practitioner of real snail mail in existence.

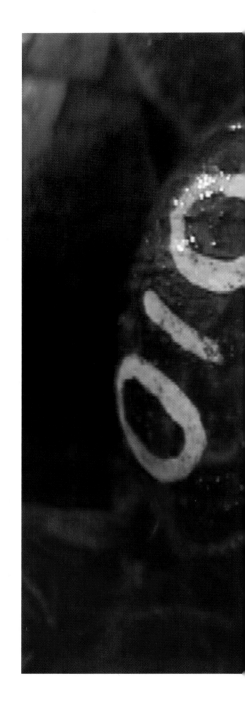

PLACES WE'VE BEEN

INDIA

Somehow the Taj Mahal manages to rise above the hype and cliché and be magnificent, although *me* in front of the Taj—I'm not so sure. But at the same time the Taj says very little about modern India: the intense colours, the traffic chaos, the humanity everywhere … you simply cannot prepare for it. Even though we were moving from one historic (or scenic) site to another, I couldn't help feeling that our few days there were hopelessly inadequate, that, like the blind men touching the elephant, we might have sampled India, depicted it

EIGHT

Buster and Me

One of the most charming things
about dogs is that they can boast
many millennia of shared history
with us. They hung around the
campfire at first, eventually
integrating themselves seamlessly
into human culture. My dog,
Buster, apparently thinks
that he's the ultimate product,
the zenith of that process.

N OF 1

N OF 1, OR N=1, IS A LABEL GIVEN TO AN experiment with only one subject, a phrase usually used disparagingly to dismiss anyone who claims to have scientific evidence based on a single data point. My favourite N of 1 is my dog, Buster. Of all the animals we've featured on *Daily Planet* over the years, he is, understandably, the best, to my mind. A standard poodle of considerable age (by the time you read this he'll be fifteen), he has endured hours of on-camera work with the dignity typical of his breed. More important, every time I've recruited him to demonstrate some piece of research on dog behaviour, he has managed to prove it wrong, at least for N=1. Even so, his reluctance to confirm what others are finding simply illustrates the folly of expecting living things to conform to our expectations. Besides, it's just TV, not science!

My favourite example was a piece of doggy mathematics. The question was, If you throw a stick into the water for a dog to fetch, and the stick is either off to the left or the right, not

▶ I know it looks like Buster's listening to me describe the possibilities, but he's really just looking at the stick.

▲ See? I told you he was just interested in the stick.

straight out, what will the dog do? Run along the shore until the stick is directly in front, then swim out to it? Or use geometry to angle toward the stick, thus cutting down on the distance travelled? The latter might make sense, but don't forget that a dog can move much more quickly on shore than in the water, so the decision to angle toward the stick should take that into account. This would force the dog to do a tricky calculation of speed versus distance, theoretically resulting in a path that would take him partway along the beach, then into the water, taking advantage of both speed on land and angle of approach.

What better breed to sort all this out than a standard poodle? They are universally judged to be one of the smartest dogs on the planet, so we took Buster down to Lake Ontario and sketched in the sand the alternative routes (I didn't notice if he was checking them out). Then I heaved the stick into the cold, cold waters. And, of course, Buster chose none of the alternatives.

He did indeed run along the beach as if he were calculating the shortest combination of time/distance, but then … he stopped dead. And waited. Brilliant, I thought. He just doesn't want to go into the water because it's too cold, and he's decided that while the stick is attractive, it's not *that* attractive. Then another, even more ingenious possibility occurred to me: he's waiting for the waves to bring the stick in. What a dog! But then the desire for the stick apparently overwhelmed him and he waded in to retrieve it, meaning that it wasn't too cold, and he wasn't waiting. He was just being N of 1.

I've always been fascinated by the contagiousness of yawns. Research years ago by Robert Provine at the University of Maryland showed that when a group starts to yawn, it's not because they're not getting enough oxygen, or because they have too much carbon dioxide in their blood. No, contagious yawning is a social signal of some kind, one that's very hard to ignore. You don't even have to see or hear the yawns, just read about them—as you're doing right now!

Psychologists, anthropologists, and primatologists have struggled to explain why this should be so. I've seen suggestions that dominant primates would yawn to coordinate bedding down for the night, or, conversely, to rouse the troop in the morning, but as far as I can tell there's been no convincing theory. Even brain imaging hasn't shed much light on the phenomenon, other than to suggest that it bypasses conscious awareness. So you can image how delighted I was to see a report that dogs will yawn in response to human yawns. It made sense: the single attribute that defines dogs best is how strongly their behaviour is tuned to ours. Naturally we took Buster out to the park, where we did our best to persuade him to look at me as I yawned, over and over again. Giant, jaw-cracking yawns.

I don't know what it was—maybe he was engrossed in thoughts about how to retrieve a stick from the water—but there wasn't even a hint of a poodle yawn. Nothing. If anything he looked bored, and no, even I wasn't going to interpret that as *wanting* to yawn.

You'd consider that a failure, wouldn't you? Or would you? Since that original claim, a second report in the scientific literature failed to find any good evidence that dogs are subject to the contagious yawn effect. Buster was obviously just alerting me to that possibility.

Much dog research has been predicated on the idea that through the 10,000-plus years that dogs have been with us, they've

◀ Yawning is contagious, for dogs as well as humans. Or is it? I think he's trying to tell me something.

gradually adapted to humans and have tuned their behaviour to be in sync with ours. Reach out and point to something, and a dog will follow the direction of your finger, but a wolf won't, and a chimp might not either. Dogs have come to know what that gesture means. I came across a nice piece of research along this line where it was argued that a dog can be persuaded to choose a smaller bowl of food over a larger one *if* the owner makes a huge fuss over the smaller bowl. Sounds like good television, right? So after struggling to get Buster to sit while I set up the experiment, I put a single treat in one bowl and eight treats in another, and set them down on the floor. He, naturally, went to the eight-treat bowl first (but of course cleaned out both ASAP).

Then the crucial part of the experiment: same bowls, same numbers of treats, but this time, as I was putting them down, I lavished attention on the single treat, holding it in my hands and practically shouting, "Ohh, this looks sooooo good, oh Buster, I can't believe how delicious this looks, ohh, I want to eat it myself...." You get the picture. I sat down, and he went straight to the bowl I had fussed over, ate the single treat, then swung around and ate the other eight.

The experiment worked perfectly, but I have to admit that from a scientific point of view, it was flawed for more reasons than the fact I did it just once with N=1. Here's why: for some reason I switched the positions of the bowls between trials, meaning that really he might have just been going to the bowl on the right no matter what. But I prefer to believe that it actually worked. As I said at the time, "I can't believe this worked. He went to his master's choice: sometimes it's better to be social than to be greedy." Of course, what I should have said was, it's better to be social—if you're going to get better food!

We've used Buster in many other studies, just to remind viewers that, yes, we are talking about dogs. There was the study that showed that dogs wag their tails more to the

▲ Apparently, for a dog at least, it pays to be both social and greedy.

Buster is well known in my family for stealing food from a kitchen counter whenever he can.

right when they see their masters, but more to the left when they encounter a dominant dog. Another revealed that the bonding hormone oxytocin rises in the blood of dog owners who've just stared deeply into their dogs' eyes, showing that it's not just that the animals have adapted to life with us, but also vice versa.

Finally, when we attempted the television version of one of the most intriguing studies involving dogs and people, Buster outwitted me again. This study claimed that dog owners are deluding themselves when they think their dogs exhibit signs of guilt or shame after they've done something wrong. The owners "see" behaviour that isn't really there. The setup was simple: dog owners were told that when they'd been out of the room, their dog had eaten a forbidden treat—or not. Indeed, in some cases it had; other times it had not. The important thing was that the owners were misled: what they were told wasn't necessarily what had happened. They were then asked to judge how guilty their dog looked, and, naturally, if they thought their dog has stolen the treat, they read guilt into its behaviour. The owners' response depended on what they *thought* the dog had done, not what had actually happened. Of course as soon as a dog is chastised, it will look downcast, thus reinforcing the owner's belief that it's guilt-ridden.

Buster is well known in my family for stealing food from a kitchen counter whenever he can. So we perched a slice of bread with peanut butter right on the edge of the counter, started the camera rolling, and left the kitchen, quietly closing the door behind us. We had done the same thing a few years before and had captured him in the act of theft within a minute. However, this time something weird happened. After hearing no sounds from the kitchen, I peeked in through a crack in the door, and there he was, staring at me, the slice of bread untouched. I closed the door again, and this time we retreated further. Again, nothing. Minutes passed, and we finally had to abandon the idea of shooting this story, simply because he wouldn't touch the slice of bread.

There's a happy ending, though. When I got home from work that night, Buster had somehow retrieved the entire loaf of bread from the top of the microwave and had eaten it all, breaking a glass casserole dish in the process. And no trace of guilt anywhere on his muzzle.

▲ He fell for it this time, but years later, when we tried it again, he outsmarted us.

ACKNOWLEDGMENTS

WRITING A BOOK LIKE THIS IS AN UNUSUAL EXPERIENCE, BECAUSE SO MANY people have not just lent a helping hand but actually created it. Penny Park, a long-time colleague of mine, got the ball rolling by performing what could only be called a tour de force of research, watching years and years' worth of video (fifteen years' worth, actually, from a *daily* science show!) and making flawless judgments of which episodes should be included in this book. Her work shaped the content much more strongly than did mine.

When Penny moved on, Pia Ferrari took over. Pia is relatively new to the business, but you'd never know it: she threw herself into the project with skill, tenacity, insight, and patience. The credit for the absolutely stunning range of images in this book goes to her: she twisted the researchers' arms to send them. She kept this ambitious and unwieldy project on track and on time, which sometimes demanded dragging the writer along with her.

I admit to being that writer, but even there I have to defer to the people who were the real sources for the stories: the producers at Discovery Channel's *Daily Planet.* They are the ones who turn an experiment, an adventure, or even a crazy invention into a television story: no producers, no stories, no book. They are, in no particular order: Barb Ustina, Ben Schaub, Nicole Sen, Mark Stevenson, Kelly McKeown, Jenn Sunnerton, Frances MacKinnon, Carol McGrath, Cindy Bahadur, Sean McShane, Larissa Moore, Sonya Buyting, Ivan Semeniuk, Deanna Kraus, Steven Sheahan, Jennifer Scott, Laura Boast, Shannon Bentley, Agatha Rachpaul, Seonaid Eggett, Jeff Berman, Amanda Buckiewicz, Doug Crosbie, Alix MacDonald, Alex Bystram, Beth Macdonell, Henry Kowalski, Steven Hunt, John Morrison, Mark Miller, Jeff Blundell, Lori Belanger, Jane Mingay, and Rob Davidson. God help me if I've forgotten anyone—I didn't intend to.

Watching the videos reminded me of the huge contributions of my co-hosts through the years, especially Natasha Stillwell, Gillian Deacon, Jane Gilbert, Judy Halladay, Patty Kim, Kim Jagtiani, and Ziya Tong.

Many others, of course, contribute to the production of a television story: CTV Creative, cameramen like our two staff shooters Jay Kemp and Ross MacIntosh, graphics experts Kevin Francisco and Matthew Knegt, and a host of editors.

A book like this cannot arise out of thin air (if it did, we'd do a story on it). At Penguin Group (Canada), Andrea Magyar, Helen Smith, Chrystal Kocher, David Ross, and Marcia Gallego ensured that this would actually become a book. At Discovery Channel, Jeff MacDonald, Ken MacDonald, Jennifer Preston, James Fletcher, Edwina Follows, Gloria Matthews, Spencer Griffith, and Tim Baiden encouraged, facilitated, and kept a watchful eye over the progression of the project. Paul Lewis's foreword not only captures the spirit of intellectual fun that this book is all about but reflects his encouragement.

I am indebted to Mary Anne Moser for, among other things, allowing me to sit and write while she went snowboarding.

And, finally, there would be no stories at all without the ingenuity and hard work of the scientists, inventors, and engineers in this book. Some of them went far beyond simply agreeing to be part of it, and provided advice and valuable additional material. Among them I'd like to acknowledge especially John Mombourquette, Gail Patricelli, Sheila Patek and the Patek Lab, Melitta Franceschini, Fred Leak, Wes Wynne, Wally Wallington, John Nyakatura, Kaye Baudinette, Michael Persinger, Robert Higgins, Craig Calfee, Karen Warkentin, Phillip Greer, Jim Meaney, Glen Turpin, and Stephen Eales.

INDEX

lizards, *148–49,* 148–153, *150, 153*
Loy, Tom, 203
Lunenberg, Nova Scotia, 256–60

M

Maclean, Steve, 182, *182*
magnetic fields, and brain, 58–59
mantis shrimp, 214–19, *216*
Mars rovers, 118
Max Planck Institute, 170
Meaney, Jim, 38–41, *40*
meiofauna in sand, 95–96
Meteor Crater, *114–15*
microorganisms, 245
microwave radiation, 185
Missouri (replica), 64, 66
Mombourquette, John, *127*
monkeys, *46,* 166–167, *167*
Montandon, Adam, 234, 235
moose, robotic, *119, 125,* 125–27, *126*
Morris, Stephen, 96, *96,* 96–97, 98
mortar and pestle, modernized, 12–13
Moscow, 192
mummy, natural, 196–203

N

National Museum of Natural History, 96
NeuroArm, 118
Nomex, 226
Northern Lights, 252–53, 252–55, *254, 255*
North Island Wildlife Recovery Centre, 35, 36, *37*
North Texas Battle Group, 62–67, *66*
Nova, 6

Nova Scotia Department of Natural Resources, 126
Nyakatura, John, 135–36

O

odours and decomposition, 207–208
Ontario Volunteer Emergency Response Team (OVERT), 207
organisms
   marine, and disease, 134–35
   in sand, *95,* 95–96
Ormond, Neal, 42–44, *44*
Ötzi the iceman, *196–97,* 196–203, *198, 199, 200*
oxygen, consumption in wallabies, 138

P

Panama Canal, *10*
pandas, *140–41,* 140–45
parrots, African Grey, *128,* 129
Patek, Sheila, 214, 216, 217
Patricelli, Gail, *121,* 121–24
Payette, Julie, 178, *178*
Pengrowth Saddledome, 217, *218*
Pepperberg, Irene, *128,* 129
Perseus, 259, 260
Persinger, Dr. Michael, 56–59
phenomena, otherworldly, 56–59
physics
   of beaches, 92–94
   of sand, 92–94, 96–97
plastic bag, for decontaminating water, 13, *13*
Pneumatipak II, 44
prayer, power of and healing, 246–50

PHOTO CREDITS

Two: Outliers

Three: Material World

Page 107 (all): Phillip Greer

Pages 108–109: *Daily Planet*

Page 110 (top): *Daily Planet*

Page 110 (bottom four images): Dynamic Shelters Inc.

Page 111: Dynamic Shelters Inc.

Pages 112–113: *Daily Planet*

Pages 114–115: John Morrison

Four: How Animals Work

Pages 116–117: *Daily Planet*

Pages 118–119 (left): Courtesy of Professor Jun Ho Oh, Professor of Mechanical Engineering, KAIST, Korea

Pages 118–119 (right): © Province of Nova Scotia, courtesy of Department of Natural Resources. Photos by Paul Darrow.

Page 120 (all): Gail Patricelli

Page 121: Manny Crisostomo/*Sacramento Bee*/ZUMA Press

Page 123: Gail Patricelli

Page 124: Isabelle Bachy

Page 125: © Province of Nova Scotia, courtesy of Department of Natural Resources. Photos by Paul Darrow.

Page 126: © Province of Nova Scotia, courtesy of Department of Natural Resources. Photos by Paul Darrow.

Page 127: © Province of Nova Scotia, courtesy of Department of Natural Resources. Photos by Paul Darrow.

Page 129: *Daily Planet*

Page 130: Andrew Gillman, University of Utah

Page 132 (left): *Daily Planet*

Page 132 (right): C. G. Farmer and Kent Sanders

Page 133: *Daily Planet*

Page 134: *Daily Planet*

Page 135: Photo by John A. Nyakatura

Page 136: Photo by John A. Nyakatura

Page 137: *Daily Planet*

Page 139: *Daily Planet*

Pages 140–141: Mark Foerster/Foerster Productions

Page 142: *Daily Planet*

Page 143: Mark Foerster/Foerster Productions

Page 144: *Daily Planet*

Page 145: *Daily Planet*

Pages 146–147: *Daily Planet*

Pages 148–149: *Daily Planet*

Page 150: *Daily Planet*

Page 151 (all): *Daily Planet*

Page 152 (all): *Daily Planet*

Page 153 (all): *Daily Planet*

Pages 154–155: George Grall/National Geographic Stock

Page 156 (left): Caveney, S; McLean, H; Surry, D (1997). "Faecal Firing in a Skipper Caterpillar Is Pressure-Driven," *The Journal of Experimental Biology* 201, p. 130

Page 156 (right): Caveney, S; McLean, H; Surry, D (1997). "Faecal Firing in a Skipper Caterpillar Is Pressure-Driven," *The Journal of Experimental Biology* 201, p. 124

Page 157: Caveney, S; McLean, H; Surry, D (1997). "Faecal Firing in a Skipper Caterpillar Is Pressure-Driven," *The Journal of Experimental Biology* 201, p. 127

Page 158: Courtesy of Tom Eisner

Page 159: Susan Middleton

Pages 160–161: *Daily Planet*

Page 162 (background): Stephen Eales

Page 162 (inset): *Daily Planet*

Page 163: *Daily Planet*

Pages 164–165: Stephen Eales

Page 167: *Daily Planet*

Pages 168–169: *Daily Planet*

Pages 170–171: *Daily Planet*

Page 172: *Daily Planet*

Page 173: *Daily Planet*

Page 174: *Daily Planet*

Page 175: *Daily Planet*

Five: Canada in Space

Pages 176–177: Giovanni Benintende/Shutterstock

Page 178: *Daily Planet*

Page 179 (top): *Daily Planet*

Page 179 (middle and bottom): Courtesy of NASA

Page 180: *Daily Planet*

Page 181 (top): *Daily Planet*

Page 181 (bottom): © Canadian Space Agency (www.asc-csa.gc.ca)

Page 182: *Daily Planet*

Page 183: Courtesy of NASA

Page 185: Philip Waterson, LBIPP, LRPS

Page 186: *Daily Planet*

Page 187: Courtesy of NASA

Page 188 (top): *Daily Planet*

Page 188 (bottom): Courtesy of NASA

Page 189 (top): *Daily Planet*

Page 189 (bottom): Courtesy of NASA

Page 190: *Daily Planet*

Page 191 (top): *Daily Planet*

Page 191 (bottom): Courtesy of NASA

Page 192 (all): *Daily Planet*

Page 193 (all): *Daily Planet*

Six: Life or Death

Pages 194–195: South Tyrol Museum of Archaeology (www.iceman.it)

Pages 196–197: South Tyrol Museum of Archaeology (www.iceman.it)

Page 198 (main): South Tyrol Museum of Archaeology (www.iceman.it)

Page 198 (inset): Courtesy of Austrian Police

Page 199: South Tyrol Museum of Archaeology (www.iceman.it)

Page 200: South Tyrol Museum of Archaeology (www.iceman.it)

Page 201 (top): Copyright © 2008 Bata Shoe Museum, Toronto
    (Photo: Hal Roth)

Page 201 (bottom): South Tyrol Museum of Archaeology (www.iceman.it)

Page 203 (all): *Daily Planet*

Pages 204–205: *Daily Planet*

Page 206 (all): *Daily Planet*

Page 207: *Daily Planet*

Pages 208–209 (top): Jason Richards, ORNL Photographer. Courtesy
of ORNL, managed for U.S. Dept. of Energy by UT-Battelle, LLC

Page 209 (bottom): *Daily Planet*

Page 211 (top): *Daily Planet*

Page 211 (bottom): Ronald van der Beek/Shutterstock

Page 212: *Daily Planet*

Page 213: Ronnie Howard/Shutterstock

Pages 214–215: Roy Caldwell, University of California, Berkeley

Page 216: Roy Caldwell, University of California, Berkeley

Page 218: VanHart/Shutterstock

Page 219: Original images courtesy of *Daily Planet,* graphic courtesy
of Ann Sanderson, CrowleArt

Pages 220–221: worldswildlifewonders/Shutterstock

Page 223: Karen M. Warkentin

Pages 224–225: *Daily Planet*

Page 226: *Daily Planet*

Page 227 (top): *Daily Planet*

Page 227 (bottom): Mark Ackerman

Pages 228–229: *Daily Planet*

Seven: Extraordinary Science

Pages 230–231: Simon Burt (www.simonburtphotography.com)

Pages 232–233: © Telegraph Media Group Limited 2005/Christopher Jones

Page 234: *Daily Planet*

Page 235 (all): Art by Neil Harbisson

Page 237: Courtesy of Ray Kurzweil

Pages 238–239: *Daily Planet*

Page 240: *Daily Planet*

Page 241 (all): *Daily Planet*

Page 242: *Daily Planet*

Page 243 (all): *Daily Planet*

Page 245: *Daily Planet*

Pages 246–247: *Daily Planet*

Page 249: *Daily Planet*

Page 251: *Daily Planet*

Pages 252–253: The Thomson Collection © Art Gallery of Ontario

Page 254: Replica sketch by CTV Creative

Page 255: Replica sketch by CTV Creative

Pages 256–257: Courtesy of David Turner and Dan Majaess

Page 258 (top): *Daily Planet*

Page 258 (bottom): Courtesy of David Turner and Dan Majaess

Page 259: *Daily Planet*

Page 260: *Daily Planet*

Page 261: Courtesy of David Turner and Dan Majaess

Page 262: Vicky Isley and Paul Smith (boredomresearch); courtesy of
    [DAM]Berlin

Pages 264–265: *Daily Planet*

Page 266 (inset): *Daily Planet*

Pages 266–267: Pius Lee/Shutterstock

Pages 268–269: Courtesy of Lorella Zanetti, Lorella Zanetti Photography

Page 271: *Daily Planet*

Page 272: *Daily Planet*

Page 273: *Daily Planet*

Page 274: *Daily Planet*

Page 276 (all): *Daily Planet*

Page 277 (all): *Daily Planet*